THE LANGUAGE OF MATHEMATICS IN SCIENCE

A Guide for Teachers of 11–16 Science

The Association for Science Education (ASE) is the largest subject association in the UK. As the professional body for all those involved in science education from pre-school to higher education, the ASE provides a national network supported by a dedicated staff team. Members include teachers, technicians and advisers. The Association plays a significant role in promoting excellence in teaching and learning of science in schools and colleges. More information is available at www.ase.org.uk.

The Nuffield Foundation is an endowed charitable trust that aims to improve social well-being in the widest sense. It funds research and innovation in education and social policy and also works to build capacity in education, science and social science research. The Nuffield Foundation has funded this project, but the views expressed are those of the authors and not necessarily those of the Foundation. More information is available at www.nuffieldfoundation.org.

First published 2016

Association for Science Education
College Lane, Hatfield, Herts AL10 9AA
Tel: +44 (0)1707 28300
Email: info@ase.org.uk
Website: www.ase.org.uk

ISBN 978 0 86357 455 9

Author: Richard Boohan

ASE project team: Marianne Cutler, Richard Boohan, Richard Needham

Mathematics advisers to project team: Andrew Noyes and Geoffrey Wake

Steering group: Robin Millar (chair, University of York), Jeremy Hodgen (University of Nottingham), Andrew Hunt (formerly Nuffield Curriculum Centre), Jane Imrie (NCETM), Cheryl Lloyd (Nuffield Foundation), Rosalind Mist (Royal Society), Michael Reiss (UCL Institute of Education), Clare Thomson (Institute of Physics), Brian Cartwright (observer, HMI), Janet Holloway (observer, Ofqual).

Awarding organisations: Matthew Bennett (AQA), Kathryn Booth (Edexcel), Natasha Chowdhury (OCR), Helen Francis (WJEC), Stella Paes (AQA), Michelle Spiller (OCR)

Science and mathematics review panel: Peter Campbell, Brian Cartwright, Ian Galloway, Andrew Hunt, Jane Imrie, Philip Johnson, Scott Keir, Stephen Lyon, Roni Malek, Robin Millar, Robin Sutton, Mary Whitehouse

Teacher review panel and others providing feedback: Dan Abbott, Christine Abdelmoutaleb, Damian Ainscough, Sarah Albenna, Nicola Arthur, Matthew Benyohai, Tim Bridle, Stephen Burrowes, Miriam Chaplin, Antony Checkett, Anthony Clowser, Steve Cooke, Ally Davies, Emma Dooley, Pat Dower, George Duoblys, John East, Stuart Farmer, Carolyne Gerrard, Alastair Gittner, Stephanie Gordon, Mark Harrison, Robin Hartley, Louise Herbert, Sarah Hinsley, George Hurst, Mike Jackson, Bob Kiddle, Mark Levesley, Calvin Lim, Claudia Patricia López, Nicola McGrath, Eliza McIntosh, Stewart McKane, Colin Oates, Muhsin Ogretme, Simon Richards, Emma Rivers, Dave Rockett, John Ryan, Alison Sefton, Annette Simpson, David Staniforth, Andreas Stockey, Alaric Thompson, Heather Thomson, Marc Tillotson, Ed Walsh, Gary Ward, Dorothy Warren, Colleen Wells, Nicola Wilberforce, Leonard Winning, Gordon Wright

Copy-editing and typesetting: Andrew Welsh (www.andrew-welsh.com)

Cover design: Colin Barker

Cover image: Snowflake © Sergey Kichigin (www.dreamstime.com)

Printed by Streets Process Colour Printers, Baldock

Contents

Introduction: the language of mathematics in science

The aim of this book is to enable teachers, publishers, awarding bodies and others to achieve a common understanding of important terms and techniques related to the use of mathematics in the science curriculum for pupils aged 11–16.

Background

This publication was produced as part of the ASE/Nuffield project *The Language of Mathematics in Science* in order to support teachers of 11–16 science in the use of mathematical ideas in the science curriculum. This is an area that has been a matter of interest and debate for many years. Some of the concerns have been about problems of consistency in terminology and approaches between the two subjects. The project built on the approach of a previous ASE/Nuffield publication, *The Language of Measurement*, and the aims are rather similar: to achieve greater clarity and agreement about the way the ideas and terminology are used in teaching and assessment.

Two publications have been produced during the project. This publication, *The Language of Mathematics in Science: A Guide for Teachers of 11–16 Science*, provides an overview of relevant ideas in secondary school mathematics and where they are used in science. It aims to clarify terminology and to indicate where there may be problems in student understanding. The publication includes explanations of key ideas and terminology in mathematics, along with a glossary of terms. A second publication, *The Language of Mathematics in Science: Teaching Approaches*, uses teachers' accounts to outline different ways that science and mathematics departments have worked together, and illustrates various teaching approaches with examples of how children respond to different learning activities.

About this publication

In developing this publication, the starting point was to identify relevant mathematical key words that should be included in the glossary. These were selected on the basis that the ideas form an important aspect of the current 11–16 science curriculum. Many familiar terms that pupils should know from elementary work in mathematics are not included (e.g. multiplication), although some terms are included that are currently not commonly used in 11–16 science but are potentially useful for science teachers to know about (e.g. box plot). The definitions of the selected key words are given in the Glossary for teachers at the end of this publication.

Definitions are useful for clarity, but only go so far. The major part of the publication consists of ten chapters, each explaining 'clusters' of these key words so that their use can be seen in context. The chapters and the associated key words are based around 'kinds of things we do in science'. For example, 'Collecting data' is concerned with terms such as 'quantity', 'value', 'unit' and 'variable'; 'Dealing with variability' is concerned with terms such as 'distribution', 'uncertainty', 'mean' and 'outlier'.

The clusters of key words are included in a panel at the start of each chapter, and a complete list of these can be seen in the Overview of chapters. Note that a number of key words appear in more than one chapter. Within the chapters, the key words are indicated in **_bold italic_** text and each of these appears as an entry in the glossary. Each entry has references back to the relevant sections in the chapters, so the glossary also acts as an index.

The aims of the publication are to:

- provide an overview of the mathematics relevant to science that may be studied by pupils at secondary school
- indicate the relevance of the ideas to the activities undertaken in secondary school science
- clarify the meaning of the terms used where there are common misunderstandings or where there are different meanings in different contexts
- indicate as appropriate where there may be student misconceptions and problems in understanding
- identify, where relevant, approaches taken in mathematics teaching that may influence what is done in science lessons.

Although there is some discussion of the details of mathematical techniques and procedures, this is not intended to be comprehensive, since further information can be found in relevant mathematics references. Instead, the focus is on an understanding of the underlying principles of the use of mathematics in school science. The intention is that the booklet will be a useful day-to-day reference that teachers can use to clarify ideas, as well as being used to inform the production of schemes of work and in promoting collaboration with the mathematics department.

Mathematics and science

Consistency between mathematics and science is clearly desirable wherever possible: it is unhelpful to have arbitrary differences in approaches and terminology between the subjects. This publication has been developed in collaboration with both science and mathematics educators in order to ensure that the usage of the language is correct and, as far as possible, consistent across subjects. However, mathematics and science are different disciplines, each with its own purposes, traditions and practices, and this leads to some differences in the way language is used.

In science, we are used to terms such as 'power', 'force', 'pressure' and so on having different meanings in everyday language, compared with the precise definitions used in science. There are fewer words in the language than meanings in the world to be expressed. It is not that science is correct and everyday language is wrong, but that words are used in different ways in different contexts. It is important for pupils to be able to recognise these differences when they move between contexts.

In a similar way, there are differences in the way that some terms are used in mathematics and science. One example is the term 'line', which has a more precise meaning in mathematics than the way it is often used in science. In mathematics, a line is, by definition, straight. In science, however, it is quite common to talk about 'straight lines' and 'curved lines'. Changing habitual ways of talking is hard: a good compromise in science might be to continue to refer to 'straight lines', but to talk of 'curves' rather than 'curved lines'. Another example is the use of the word 'histogram'. In mathematics, this refers to a display of a distribution of data in which the bars represent 'frequency density' for each class interval; in science, the bars of a histogram normally represent 'frequency'. Teachers and pupils need to be aware of such differences in usage between mathematics and science. Where these differences exist, they are indicated in the glossary and discussed in the relevant chapters.

In addition, some mathematical terms have multiple meanings in science; for example, 'range' may refer to the 'range of a measuring instrument', the 'range of an axis on a graph' or the 'range of a variable'. Other such examples include 'scale', 'coefficient' and 'variable'. Again, these differences in meanings are given in the glossary.

Collaboration between mathematics and science departments is clearly helpful in achieving a common understanding and in sequencing the introduction and use of mathematical ideas in an appropriate way. It is hoped that this publication will be useful in stimulating and supporting such discussions. However, it is beyond the scope of the publication to recommend details of what should be taught and when: this will depend on particular circumstances. Similarly, it is beyond the scope of the publication to give an indication of what range of knowledge or skills might be expected of pupils of different ages. While the current curricula in the UK have been taken into account in developing this publication, it has not been the intention to make any specific references to any particular programmes of study or assessment arrangements.

Thinking about purposes and using judgement

Although this book is designed to be used as a reference source, with sufficient cross-references that any section can be read independently, there is also a narrative that runs through it. Chapters 1 and 2 are concerned with the collection and processing of data, and Chapters 3 and 4 deal with the representation of data in tables, charts and graphs. Chapters 5 to 8 look at different kinds of relationships, from those where one variable is directly proportional to another to those where there is a good deal more variability in the data values. Finally, Chapter 9 focuses on the use of algebraic equations in science, and Chapter 10 looks at some of the areas of science that are also addressed in the mathematics curriculum.

One of the themes that runs throughout these chapters is the importance of thinking about *purposes*. What is the purpose of drawing this graph? What is the purpose of calculating this mean? It is not about the unthinking application of techniques but about considering what makes sense in different contexts. Knowing how to apply mathematical ideas in science is often a matter of using *judgement*.

There are no 'recipes' for how to design experiments, collect data and handle results; there are also no 'rules' for when and how to use mathematical techniques in science. This does not mean that nothing can be seen as 'correct' or 'incorrect'. It is important, for example, that pupils understand the meaning of 'significant figures', can distinguish this from 'decimal places' and can correctly apply the conventional rules of rounding. This is different from deciding what is an appropriate number of significant figures, which depends on context and requires judgement. These judgements are not uninformed – there are criteria that can be learned and that can support pupils' justifications for their decisions. It is for this reason that the publication puts an emphasis on understanding the nature of the mathematical ideas, and not just the techniques.

Understanding the nature of data

One table of data may look much like another, with numbers in rows and columns. Even though two tables may show superficial similarities, there may be fundamental differences between the nature of the data in each table. Such differences are important, since the ways that data can be analysed and how they can be represented visually depend on what kind of data they are. These choices may be difficult. Drawing a bar graph requires a certain level of competence, but deciding whether a bar chart is appropriate for a particular set of data is harder. Such questions have generated a good deal of discussion during the development of this publication. While much of this may be beyond many pupils, understanding the nature of different types of data is important in designing appropriate classroom activities.

There are a wide range of terms used in statistics to describe the nature of data. Chapter 1 provides a simplified account of the key ideas, with a focus on the distinctions that are helpful to make in science and on the questions that are useful to ask. It introduces the terms 'continuous', 'discrete' and 'categorical', which are revisited in Chapter 3 in considering how to represent data. There are many ways in which data can be organised and represented – in different kinds of tables, pie charts, bar charts, line graphs, scatter graphs and so on. The choices depend on the nature of the data and the kinds of questions about the data that are of interest. A particular advantage of a computer is that it allows different choices of display to be easily explored.

An important distinction is made in Chapter 3 between 'line graphs' and 'scatter graphs'. Although in one way they are similar, with the positions of data points determined by the scales on the horizontal and vertical axes, the nature of the data is fundamentally different. For example, experiments involving two continuous variables are particularly common in the physical sciences. Such experiments lead to 'line graph' type data with variability due to measurement uncertainty. On the other hand, surveys that collect data for which the variability is due to differences between individuals are more common in the biological sciences, and lead to 'scatter graph' type data. The guidance in the publication puts a good deal of emphasis on the importance of distinguishing between these two sources of variability in data. The differences are discussed in Chapter 6, with each of these being followed up in more detail in Chapters 7 and 8.

Interestingly, when such examples have been discussed by teachers, some of the comments have been about how teachers in the biological and physical sciences have different practices when dealing with data and constructing graphs. However, it is not so much that different sciences approach data in different ways; rather, different sciences often deal with different kinds of data, and different kinds of data are analysed in different ways.

Assessment

It is beyond the scope of this publication to deal with questions such as how mathematics in science could be assessed, or what pupils of different ages might be expected to know and do. However, the emphasis in the publication on thinking about the importance of purposes and judgement has implications in considering what is useful to be assessed. For example, if a pupil is asked to plot a set of data values on a graph with pre-drawn axes and scales, and to draw a line of best fit, how could the graph be judged?

- *The position of the data points on the graph*
  This requires the pupil to use values in a table and to read each of the scales correctly, putting a mark at each of the appropriate points on the graph. The positioning of the points is a matter of being 'correct' or 'incorrect'. Other such examples where there are 'right' and 'wrong' answers include rounding a value to a given number of significant figures, evaluating an expression and calculating the gradient of a straight line on a graph.

- *The choice of the line of best fit*
  While there may be some very obvious 'bad lines of fit', it is very unlikely that there would be a unique 'line of best fit': the choice requires judgement. Deciding on the position of a straight line, or whether to draw a straight line or a curve, or whether to include the origin, involves thinking about the meaning of the data and depends on the context. Other examples involving the use of judgement include deciding on an appropriate number of significant figures for a calculated value, choosing what kind of chart or graph to draw, and identifying which data values should be considered as outliers.

- *The symbols used for plotting the data points*
  This is a matter of convention, and there are various arguments for favouring one type of symbol over another. Pupils may meet different conventions in different published sources so they should be aware of this. However, while it is important for a publisher to have a consistent house style in a publication, it should not be a matter of importance for pupils to follow any particular convention. Other examples include the use of brackets or the solidus with units in the axis labels on a graph, or the use of words or letters for variables in a formula.

In assessing what pupils can do, it is important to distinguish between their competence in using particular techniques and the quality of their reasoning about how to use them. While there are no 'hard-and-fast rules' for how to draw a line of best fit or for the appropriate number of significant figures of a calculated value, this does not mean that 'anything goes'. This publication emphasises the kinds of considerations to be taken into account in order to make sensible judgements.

Process of development of this publication

The ASE began this project in summer 2014, after gaining funding from the Nuffield Foundation. The work of the project was informed by the advice of a steering group, and successive drafts of this publication were reviewed by a panel of science and mathematics educators with expertise in this area, and feedback obtained from a variety of groups of science teachers. During the project, discussions took place with representatives of the awarding organisations, who have been supportive of the approaches taken in this publication. An important consideration was that the recommendations in this publication should be realistic in practice, so the concluding stage of the process was a review of the draft guidance by a large panel of teachers before the production of the final publication. The time and effort spent by so many people in providing advice over the course of the project is much appreciated, and the quality of the publication has improved greatly as a result of it.

Further references on terminology and conventions

The following publications in particular were used to inform the use of terminology and conventions in this publication, and the definitions in the glossary.

1. *The Language of Measurement: Terminology Used in School Science Investigations* (2010). Hatfield: Association for Science Education. ISBN 978 0 86357 424 5.
   This publication contains a glossary, and selected terms and definitions from it are also included in the glossary of *The Language of Mathematics in Science*. Although there is common ground, duplication is avoided and the two publications should be seen as complementary.

2. *Signs, Symbols & Systematics: The ASE Companion to 16–19 Science* (2000). Hatfield: Association for Science Education. ISBN 978 0 86357 312 6.
   This publication is the definitive guide to a wide range of factual information related to 11–19 science education (and not just the 16–19 range suggested by the title). Of particular relevance to the areas covered by *The Language of Mathematics in Science* are sections on SI units, physical quantities, values of constants, and so on.

3. *Mathematics Glossary for Teachers in Key Stages 1 to 3* (2014). National Centre for Excellence in the Teaching of Mathematics.
   Many of the definitions in the glossary of *The Language of Mathematics in Science* are based on the NCETM glossary, as well as on the earlier QCA glossary for key stages 1 to 4, from which the NCETM version was adapted. It is available from the NCETM website (www.ncetm.org.uk/public/files/17308038/National+Curriculum+Glossary.pdf).

Overview of chapters

Chapter 1 Collecting data	
1.1 Measuring and counting 1.2 Measurement, resolution and significant figures 1.3 Characteristics of different types of data 1.4 Naming different types of data 1.5 Where do data come from?	**Key words:** quantitative data, qualitative data, quantity, value, unit, resolution, scale, significant figures, range, variable, continuous, discrete, categorical, integer, experiment, survey, independent variable, dependent variable, control variable, factor, time series, raw data, primary data, secondary data
Chapter 2 Doing calculations and representing values	
2.1 Calculations and units 2.2 Fractions and decimals 2.3 Rounding and significant figures 2.4 Calculating means 2.5 Index notation and powers 2.6 Dealing with very large and very small values 2.7 Approximations and orders of magnitude	**Key words:** unit, quantity, compound measure, base unit, derived unit, variable, decimal, fraction, significant figures, round, integer, recurring decimal, decimal place, mean, arithmetic mean, index notation, index, power, exponent, square, cube, square root, cube root, reciprocal, unit prefix, standard form, standard index form, scientific notation, power of 10, order of magnitude, approximation, estimate
Chapter 3 Choosing how to represent data	
3.1 Using tables to collect and present data 3.2 Using tables to process data 3.3 Presenting data visually 3.4 Charts showing a quantity categorised by one factor 3.5 Charts showing a quantity categorised by two factors 3.6 Line graphs and scatter graphs: two related quantities 3.7 Bar charts and line graphs	**Key words:** variable, unit, raw data, categorical, discrete, continuous, factor, frequency, frequency table, grouped data, two-way table, pie chart, bar chart, grouped bar chart, stacked bar chart, independent variable, dependent variable, data point, horizontal axis, vertical axis, line graph, gradient, time series, scatter graph
Chapter 4 Drawing charts and graphs	
4.1 The important features of a chart or a graph 4.2 Choosing the axes 4.3 Choosing the range of each axis 4.4 Ranges and scales 4.5 Choosing a good scale 4.6 Labels and units 4.7 Plotting points and finding values 4.8 Reading scales	**Key words:** line graph, bar chart, scatter graph, independent variable, dependent variable, time series, axis, horizontal axis, vertical axis, x-axis, y-axis, origin, range, scale, tick mark, tick mark label, axis label, unit, data point, coordinate, x-coordinate, y-coordinate
Chapter 5 Working with proportionality and ratio	
5.1 Meaning of proportional 5.2 Proportionality and visual representation 5.3 Interpretation of gradient 5.4 Proportionality and algebraic representation 5.5 Proportional relationships in science 5.6 Ratios 5.7 Proportional reasoning and ratios 5.8 Percentages 5.9 Scale drawings and images	**Key words:** proportional, directly proportional, line graph, origin, gradient, slope, horizontal axis, vertical axis, x-axis, y-axis, x-coordinate, y-coordinate, rate, constant, constant of proportionality, reciprocal, inverse, inversely proportional, ratio, percentage, scale, scale drawing, scale factor, linear dimension

Chapter 6 Dealing with variability

6.1	Where does variability come from?	**Key words:** variability, random error, true value, uncertainty, population, sample, distribution, histogram, batch, class interval, frequency, average, mean, arithmetic mean, median, mode, spread, range, quartile, interquartile range, box plot, outlier, anomaly, probability, independent events, combined events, risk
6.2	Variability and measurement uncertainty	
6.3	Variability in a population of individuals	
6.4	Displaying larger sets of values	
6.5	How big is a typical value?	
6.6	How much do the values vary?	
6.7	Comparing shapes of distributions	
6.8	Are there any unusual values?	
6.9	Basic ideas in probability	
6.10	Estimating risks	
6.11	Interpreting reports about risk	

Chapter 7 Looking for relationships: line graphs

7.1	Types of relationship and shapes of line graphs	**Key words:** line graph, variable, linear, linear relationship, non-linear, gradient, origin, intercept, proportional, rate, line of best fit, interpolation, extrapolation, outlier
7.2	Developing a descriptive language	
7.3	Gradients and rates of change	
7.4	Lines of best fit: linear relationships	
7.5	Interpolation and extrapolation on a line graph	
7.6	Origin and intercepts: the meaning of where a fitted line starts	
7.7	When a straight line does not fit all the points	

Chapter 8 Looking for relationships: batches and scatter graphs

8.1	Different kinds of relationship	**Key words:** population, sample, random sample, batch, variability, stem-and-leaf diagram, histogram, box plot, median, quartile, range, interquartile range, outlier, percentile, scatter graph, variable, correlation, line of best fit
8.2	Populations and samples	
8.3	Analysing a batch of data	
8.4	Dealing with more than one batch of data	
8.5	Comparing batches of data	
8.6	Judging whether a difference is significant	
8.7	Relationships between variables: scatter graphs and correlation	
8.8	Drawing a line of best fit on a scatter graph	

Chapter 9 Scientific models and mathematical equations

9.1	Equations, formulae and expressions	**Key words:** equation, algebraic equation, formula, expression, variable, constant, coefficient, brackets, order of operations, subject of a formula, proportional, directly proportional, constant of proportionality, linear relationship, linear equation, inversely proportional, exponential relationship, inverse square relationship, line graph, rate, intercept, gradient, tangent, area under the line (on a graph)
9.2	Variables, constants and coefficients	
9.3	Operations and symbols	
9.4	Calculations using formulae: order of operations	
9.5	The real-world meaning of a formula	
9.6	Rearranging formulae involving addition and subtraction	
9.7	Rearranging formulae involving multiplication and division	
9.8	Rearranging other formulae	
9.9	Calculations without formulae	
9.10	Use of 'calculation triangles'	
9.11	Mathematical equations and relationships in science	
9.12	Graphs of quantities against time: gradients	
9.13	Graphs of rates against time: area under the line	

Chapter 10 Mathematics and the real world

10.1	Mass and weight	**Key words:** mass, weight, area, volume, square, cuboid, cube, scale drawing, scale factor, linear dimension, cross-sectional area, surface area, surface area : volume ratio, radius, diameter, circumference, scalar, vector, distance, displacement, speed, velocity, gradient, distance–time graph, displacement–time graph, speed–time graph, velocity–time graph, area under the line (on a graph)
10.2	Length, area and volume	
10.3	Scale factor, cross-sectional area and surface area	
10.4	Circles and spheres	
10.5	Scalars and vectors: distance and displacement	
10.6	Movement of objects: speed and velocity	
10.7	Gradients of lines on speed–time and velocity–time graphs	
10.8	Area under the line on speed–time and velocity–time graphs	

1 Collecting data

> **Key words:** quantitative data, qualitative data, quantity, value, unit, resolution, scale, significant figures, range, variable, continuous, discrete, categorical, integer, experiment, survey, independent variable, dependent variable, control variable, factor, time series, raw data, primary data, secondary data.

Science is built, fundamentally, on observations of the world around us. In pure mathematics, numbers are often treated as abstract; however, in science, numbers are associated with values related to the real world. So, in thinking about the use of mathematics in science, a fitting place to start is to look at the nature of data collection.

1.1 Measuring and counting

A very obvious distinction about the types of data that can be collected is between **quantitative data** and **qualitative data**. As an example, take the data that could be collected about the pupils in a class. Measuring the heights of the pupils would produce *quantitative* data, while their eye colours would be *qualitative* data.

As its name suggests, *quantitative* data relate to a **quantity**. In this case, the quantity is 'height of pupil' and, for each pupil, there is a **value** for this quantity. The values are not just numbers. For example, if the height of a pupil is 119 cm then the value consists of a number (119) and a **unit** (cm). So, any calculation done on the *value* (119 cm) must be done on *the number and the unit*. Handling units in calculations is an important aspect of science. (See Section 2.1 *Calculations and units* on page 14 for further details.)

By contrast, the eye colours of pupils represent *qualitative* data – there are no numbers involved. If the numbers of pupils with each eye colour are *counted*, then each eye colour becomes a category with an associated numerical value. Thus, quantitative data can be generated from qualitative data. The 'eye colour of a pupil' is an *attribute of an individual* and is an example of qualitative data; the 'numbers of pupils with each eye colour' is a *variable* consisting of quantitative data.

So, there are two basic ways of collecting quantitative data – by *measuring* and by *counting*.

1.2 Measurement, resolution and significant figures

The values of measurements are limited by the **resolution** of the measuring instrument whether analogue (e.g. a ruler) or digital (e.g. an electronic balance). It is easy to do a calculation to get a number such as 2.3913043 displayed on a calculator; it is not possible, however, to use a school stopclock to record a value for a time such as 2.3913043 seconds. To do this would require an instrument with higher resolution.

A ruler generally has a **scale** that is divided into millimetres. When measuring with a ruler, it is usual to give the result to the nearest millimetre, since it is difficult by eye to judge fractions of a millimetre. The height of a sheet of A4 paper, as measured by a ruler, is 297 mm. This value has three **significant figures** – the number of digits that contribute information about the size of the value.

The number of significant figures is related to the *uncertainty* in the measurement. Reporting a measurement as '297 mm' does not imply that the 'true value' is *exactly* 297 mm, but that it is more likely to be nearer 297 mm than to 296 mm or 298 mm. (For more details about uncertainty, see Section 6.2 *Variability and measurement uncertainty* on page 51.)

Changing the units of measurement of a measured value does not change the number of significant figures. For example, the height of an A4 sheet of paper, 297 mm, could also be expressed as 29.7 cm or 0.297 m, or even as 0.000 297 km. All of these values have *three* significant figures, even though they have different numbers of digits after the decimal point. However, measuring a 2p coin with a ruler gives a result for the diameter of 26 mm. The resolution of the ruler is still the same, though in this case the value has only two significant figures.

In general, reading an analogue scale by eye will ideally produce a value with three significant figures, though sometimes it may have only two.

On a digital instrument, the values are read directly from the display. On kitchen scales reading to the nearest 1 g, the mass of a litre carton of orange juice might be displayed as 1082 g (four significant figures), while the mass of a 2p coin shows as 7 g (one significant figure). Again, the resolution of the instrument is the same, but the number of significant figures is different. For the coin, a more accurate value would be obtained using a balance with a greater resolution: such an instrument would tend to have a smaller **range**. For example, kitchen scales that read to the nearest 1 g might measure up to 5000 g, while a 'pocket-sized' balance reading to the nearest 0.001 g might only read up to 20 g. On the latter balance, the mass of a 2p coin might then be displayed as 7.154 g (four significant figures).

The 'zero' digit has an important role in expressing the number of significant figures for a value. If another coin is put on the same balance, and the display shows 7.200 g, then this should be recorded as '7.200 g' and not '7.2 g'. Writing '7.200 g' indicates that its mass was measured to the nearest '0.001 g', whereas writing '7.2 g' suggests that a balance with a lower resolution that only measured to the nearest 0.1 g was used.

On some digital instruments (e.g. multimeters), it is possible to change the range depending on the value being measured, in order to increase the resolution and obtain the maximum number of significant figures.

Note that the term 'range' is applied in a number of different ways in science – to measuring instruments, to the axes on a graph, and to the values of a set of data. (See the *Glossary for teachers* on page 119 for further details.)

The number of significant figures is an indication of the *precision* of a value. Thinking about the number of significant figures of a measured value is important when rounding the values obtained in calculations. The decision of how many significant figures should be given depends on the numbers of significant figures in the starting values. (See Section 2.3 *Rounding and significant figures* on page 16.)

For further information about the terminology related to values, units and measuring instruments, see the ASE/Nuffield publication *The Language of Measurement*.

1.3 Characteristics of different types of data

Statisticians have developed further distinctions beyond 'quantitative' and 'qualitative' to describe different types of data. For secondary school science, knowing the statistical terminology is not necessary, but it is worth being aware of some key characteristics of different types of data. The distinctions are important because different types of data can be analysed and represented in different ways.

Figures 1.1–1.4 show some examples of data. Each of the columns in these tables represents a *variable*. The following questions identify key characteristics about the variables:

- *Can the data be put into a meaningful order?*
  Quantitative data can always be put into a meaningful order (from low values to high values), but qualitative data may or may not. For example, the days of the week (in Figure 1.2) form a sequence, while the pupils' eye colours (brown, blue, etc.) have no particular order.

- *Can the data have any value or are there distinct categories?*
  There are always distinct categories for qualitative data. However, quantitative data can sometimes take on any value (e.g. length and temperature), but may have a small number of possible numerical values (often integer values, such as number of trees – there can be 3 trees or 4 trees but not 3.7 trees).

Figure 1.1 Pupils in a class

Pupil	Height (cm)	Eye colour
1	158	brown
2	148	blue
3	142	brown
4	168	brown
etc.		

Figure 1.2 Rainfall

Day	Rainfall (mm)
Sunday	0
Monday	8
Tuesday	13
Wednesday	0
etc.	

Figure 1.3 An object cooling

Time (s)	Temperature (°C)
0	59.5
30	54.3
60	51.2
90	48.4
etc.	

Figure 1.4 Tree survey

Quadrat	Number of trees
A	7
B	3
C	6
D	4

- *Are the numerical differences between values meaningful?*
  Numerical *differences* between measured quantities and counts are always meaningful. For example, in Figure 1.1, pupil 1 is 158 cm tall and pupil 2 is 148 cm tall: the difference, 10 cm, is meaningful as it represents how much taller one is than the other. Differences are also meaningful for the rainfall data and for temperature. However, although the column 'Pupil' contains the numbers 1, 2, 3 . . ., these are simply labels, and the differences between them have no meaning.

- *Are the ratios of values meaningful?*
  In Figure 1.4, it would make sense to talk in terms of the *ratios* of the numbers of trees; for example, '6 trees' are twice as many trees as '3 trees'. Comparing the sizes of values in this way would also be meaningful for heights of pupils and for rainfall.

However, for temperature it would not make sense to talk about 20 °C being twice as hot as 10 °C. The choice of the zero on the Celsius scale is arbitrary, and so ratios of temperatures measured in degrees Celsius are not meaningful.

The technical terms that are used for such scales of measurement are interval scales (differences between values are meaningful) and ratio scales (ratios of values are meaningful). A ratio scale includes the properties of an interval scale (so differences between values on a ratio scale are also meaningful).

1.4 Naming different types of data

There are several terms used in statistics to describe the characteristics of different types of data, but three terms are commonly used in secondary school mathematics: **continuous**, **discrete** and **categorical**. These terms may also be encountered in secondary school science but they are used less frequently than in mathematics.

- *Continuous data*: These are numerical data for which the values can take on any value within a certain range. *Measurement* produces continuous data; for example, the heights of pupils or the temperatures of an object.

- *Discrete data*: These are also numerical data but they can only take on certain values. *Counting* produces discrete data. Counts have whole number or **integer** values; for example, number of trees in a survey area.

- *Categorical data*: These are not numerical values so they cannot be ordered but they can be sorted into categories; for example, the eye colour of pupils.

The differences between continuous and discrete data may be less marked than their definitions suggest. Although in principle it is possible for a measurement of length or temperature (*continuous data*) to have any value, in reality a measurement will have a limited number of significant figures. For example, in Figure 1.1, the height of the first pupil is measured as 158 cm. It is quite likely that, in a sufficiently large group, there will be other pupils whose heights will also be measured as 158 cm. Similarly, in a survey counting a small sample of trees (*discrete data*), there may only be a few possible values of counts (1, 2, 3, etc.), but there could be many possible values when counting large populations. Thus, in practice, it may be that continuous and discrete data are treated rather similarly, for example in deciding whether to draw a bar chart or a line graph (see Section 3.7 *Bar charts and line graphs* on page 32).

Note that the term 'discontinuous data' is sometimes used in school science; the intention is usually to mean categorical data but the term is ambiguous and can be confusing, since there are two ways that data can be 'not continuous' (discrete and categorical).

1.5 Where do data come from?

Many scientific studies are concerned with gathering evidence about the relationships between **variables**, and can be broadly characterised as **experiments** or **surveys**.

Pupils need to be aware that both of these terms have particular meanings in science, which may be different from the way they are used in everyday life. An 'experiment' may often be seen as an unstructured and random exploration, unlike the organised and purposeful 'experiment' of science. In everyday language, the term 'survey' often suggests a study involving a questionnaire to find out about people's opinions – a meaning that is also common in the mathematics classroom. In science, the term has a broader meaning.

In the simplest kind of experiment, the experimenter changes just one variable (the *independent variable*) and observes the effect on another variable (the *dependent variable*). All other variables (*control variables*) are kept constant by the experimenter.

Surveys are used in more complex situations where it is harder to manipulate the variables, so data are collected by observing the outcomes in various conditions. There may be a number of independent variables, as well as other unknown variables that affect the outcomes. Sometimes, there is no clear distinction between independent and dependent variables, and a survey just explores whether relationships exist without thinking in terms of causation.

An independent variable is often referred to as a *factor*, particularly when it is a categorical variable. (Note that the term *factor* is also used in mathematics with an entirely different meaning. See the *Glossary for teachers* on page 119.)

In experiments or surveys where changes are observed over time, the data are called a *time series* and time is treated as the independent variable.

So, a variable may be described as '*continuous, discrete or categorical*', and as '*independent, dependent or control*'. The first set of terms relate to the *nature of the data* of a variable, while the second set refers to the role of the variable *in the context of an investigation*.

Note that, in mathematics, the term *variable* refers to a quantity that can take on a range of values and is often represented by a letter (e.g. x, y) in an algebraic equation. Much of science is concerned with algebraic modelling and uses the term 'variable' in the same way. However, in science, the term 'variable' is also used in situations where an algebraic relationship is not known. (See Section 9.2 *Variables, constants and coefficients* on page 88.)

Data collected directly from experiments or surveys, before calculations are performed, are called *raw data*. If the data are collected directly by the user, these are called *primary data*. If the data are obtained indirectly from other sources reporting raw or processed data (such as books, articles or web pages), these are *secondary data*.

2 Doing calculations and representing values

> **Key words:** unit, quantity, compound measure, base unit, derived unit, variable, decimal, fraction, significant figures, round, integer, recurring decimal, decimal place, mean, arithmetic mean, index notation, index, power, exponent, square, cube, square root, cube root, reciprocal, unit prefix, standard form, standard index form, scientific notation, power of 10, order of magnitude, approximation, estimate.

The value of a quantity such as temperature or mass is represented by a *number* and a *unit*. This chapter focuses on the ways that units are used in calculations and on how values are represented. When pupils are using values in calculations, it is important that they are also thinking about the meaning of what they are calculating (see Section 9.5 *The real-world meaning of a formula* on page 93).

2.1 Calculations and units

Doing calculations on values involves paying attention to the manipulation of not just the numbers but the **units** as well. Addition and subtraction of values can only be done if they are expressed in the *same units*. For example, it may make sense to add the masses of two objects together (say 15 g and 20 g) to give a total mass (35 g). It would not make sense to add the mass (in g) of one object to the length (in m) of another. Mass and length are different kinds of **quantity** and so cannot be added together. However, it would be possible to add the values of a mass (in g) to another mass (in ounces) if they are converted to a common unit, since they are the same kind of quantity.

If some water at 60 °C is added to some water at 20 °C, it does not make sense to add the temperatures together, even though they are the same kind of quantity expressed in the same units. The masses of the water can be added together because mass is an *extensive property* (dependent on the size of the system), but temperature is an *intensive property* (independent of the size of the system) and cannot be added in this way. It would, however, make sense to calculate the temperature rise of an object (in °C) by subtracting an initial temperature (in °C) from a final temperature (in °C).

Multiplication and division may involve *different units*. For example, if a ball rolls 8 metres along the ground in 2 seconds, its average speed can be calculated. Here, the division has been done in two steps for emphasis – first the units and then the numbers.

$$\text{average speed} = \frac{\text{distance travelled}}{\text{time taken}} = \frac{8 \text{ m}}{2 \text{ s}} = \frac{8}{2} \text{ m/s} = 4 \text{ m/s}$$

In mathematics, a quantity such as speed (e.g. in metres per second) is called a **compound measure** – it involves two measures of different types; in this case, distance and time. In science, the unit 'metres per second' or 'm/s' would be called a **derived unit**. In the International System of Units (SI), there are seven **base units** (metre, kilogram, second, ampere, kelvin, mole, candela) from which all other units are derived. Some derived units are expressed in terms of the base units (such as m/s); other derived units are given special names (e.g. the unit of force is derived from the base units but is given the name 'newton').

In science, it is good practice always to include units as part of the calculation, in order to keep track of what the numbers mean. An example of a multiplication involving a derived unit would be to calculate the mass of $10\,\text{cm}^3$ of ethanol (density $0.79\,\text{g/cm}^3$).

$$\text{mass} = \text{volume} \times \text{density}$$
$$= 10\,\text{cm}^3 \times 0.79\,\text{g/cm}^3$$
$$= 7.9\,\text{g}$$

Multiplying 10 by 0.79 gives 7.9, and multiplying cm^3 by g/cm^3 gives g (grams). Since this is an appropriate unit for mass, it provides a check that the calculation has been done correctly. It also acts as a check that a formula has been written down or rearranged correctly.

Note that not all quantities have units. Those that are derived from a ratio of the sizes of two quantities do not have units, for example relative atomic mass or refractive index.

Calculations involving chemical amounts (in moles) can often lead to confusion over the use of units. For example: What is the mass of $2\,\text{mol}$ of water molecules? The relative molecular mass of water is 18, but it is not correct to say that the mass is $2 \times 18 = 36\,\text{g}$, since the units are not consistent (the relative molecular mass has no units). It is the molar mass of water ($18\,\text{g/mol}$) that is needed for the calculation.

$$\text{mass} = \text{chemical amount} \times \text{molar mass}$$
$$= 2\,\text{mol} \times 18\,\text{g/mol}$$
$$= 36\,\text{g}$$

In post-16 physics, this kind of checking of consistency of units becomes even more important, and is known as *dimensional analysis*.

Note that, in mathematics, units in calculations are handled differently. In the above formulae, the **variables** (mass, volume, and so on) represent *values with units*, so these are part of the calculations. In mathematics, however, the variables in equations do not have units. For example, if the mass of an object is being calculated from an algebraic formula, one might represent the mass as $m\,\text{kg}$. Here, the variable 'm' represents *just a number*. If the result of the calculation is $m = 6$ then the mass of the object is $6\,\text{kg}$. Teachers and pupils need to be aware of this difference in the way that units are handled in mathematics and science.

2.2 Fractions and decimals

In scientific calculations, intermediate and final values are usually expressed as **decimals** rather than **fractions**. In mathematics, pupils learn to add, subtract, multiply and divide fractions, though this is not much used in science.

One reason for this is that, when dealing with **integers** in mathematics, it makes sense to be able to manipulate the number to produce a result expressed as a fraction that also involves integers (below left). This fraction is exact, whereas expressing this value as a decimal would, in this case, not be exact. Using numbers in this way also helps to develop an understanding of how algebraic expressions can be manipulated (below right).

$$\frac{5}{3} + \frac{3}{4} = \frac{20+9}{12} = \frac{29}{12} \qquad \frac{a}{b} + \frac{c}{d} = \frac{ad+bc}{bd}$$

This kind of algebraic manipulation of fractions would not be used in secondary science, however, when doing calculations with *measured values*. The values obtained from measurements are not exact integers, so the emphasis is on convenience of calculation. For a multi-step problem, it is generally easier to calculate intermediate values at each step, rather than to build up an expression, leaving the calculation to the last step.

2.3 Rounding and significant figures

The values used in a calculation may not all have the same number of **significant figures**. For a measured value, the number of significant figures is an indication of the *precision* of measurement. For a calculated value, the number of significant figures should reflect the precision of the values used in the calculation (see Section 1.2 *Measurement, resolution and significant figures* on page 9).

A rule of thumb for rounding

A useful rule of thumb is to **round** the result to the same number of significant figures as the measured value with the fewest significant figures. This means that the precision of the result is determined by the least precise value used in the calculation.

For example, to calculate the distance travelled in 2.73 seconds by a ball with velocity 1.4 m/s:

$$\text{distance} = \text{velocity} \times \text{time} = 1.4\,\text{m/s} \times 2.73\,\text{s} = 3.822\,\text{m} = 3.8\,\text{m}$$

The number obtained by multiplying 1.4×2.73 is 3.822, but this is then rounded to two significant figures (3.8). This is because the number in the calculation with the fewer significant figures is 1.4 (two significant figures). Rounding means replacing the calculated value with the nearest number with the appropriate number of significant figures; if the calculated value is halfway between two values with the appropriate number of significant figures then it is rounded up (e.g. 3.85 rounded to two significant figures is 3.9). Older pupils may also be introduced to the convention of writing '(to 2 s.f.)' after the final value in the above calculation. This makes explicit how the result was rounded, and also avoids the implication that two unequal values are equal (i.e. 3.822 m = 3.8 m).

Distinguishing between measured values and integers

Integers need to be handled in a different way. For example, the height of an A4 sheet of paper is 297 mm. The height of 2 sheets placed end-to-end is 594 mm (2×297 mm). This is *not* rounded to 600 mm, since the value '2' is not treated as having only one significant figure. It is an *integer*, and it is *exactly* 2 (in a sense, it has an infinite number of significant figures: 2.000 000 000...). The 'number of sheets' is a 'count' and not a 'measurement'.

Recurring decimals

Sometimes, in calculations involving division, the numerator divides exactly by the denominator (e.g. $18 / 2.4 = 7.5$). If not, the result will be a **recurring decimal** (e.g. $26 / 2.4 = 10.833\,333\,33...$), even if the recurring pattern is not apparent because the calculator display does not have sufficient digits to show this (e.g. $26/2.3 = 11.30434783\ldots$). In mathematics, recurring decimals can be represented by placing dots over the digits; this convention is not needed in science, since such results are rounded to an appropriate number of significant figures.

The meaning of zeros in a value

It is important to pay attention to the way the zero digit is used to indicate the number of significant figures for measured values and for the results from calculations. For example, if a ball with a velocity 2.0 m/s travels for 4.32 seconds, the distance is found by multiplying these two values together. The calculated value is 8.64 m. The zero digit in '2.0 m/s' means that this value has two significant figures. Rounding the calculated value to two significant figures gives 8.6 m.

Similarly, if a ball with a velocity 1.4 m/s travels for 2.86 seconds, multiplying these values together gives a result for the distance of 4.004 m. Rounding this to two significant figures gives 4.0 m. Writing this as 4 m would mean something different – it would have only one significant figure and would indicate less precision in the result.

The use of the zero digit in numbers that do not have a decimal point can be ambiguous. For example, while stating a distance as 5837 m implies that it has been measured or calculated to the nearest metre, it is not so clear what 6300 m means. Does it mean that it has only been measured to the nearest 100 m? (This would imply that the true value is nearer to 6300 m than to 6200 m or 6400 m.) Or to the nearest 10 m? Or to the nearest 1 m? Without knowing the context, it is difficult to interpret what these values mean. One solution is to re-express the value in a different unit. For example, in this case, if km were used, the difference between 6.300 km and 6.3 km would be clear. Another solution is to express the value using standard form (see Section 2.6 *Dealing with very large and very small values* on page 20).

Using judgement when adding values

Judgement is necessary in using the rule of thumb when adding values, as the two examples below illustrate.

If the mass of a coin is 7.17 g then the mass of two such coins would be best expressed as 14.34 g (and not rounded to 14.3 g, even though the original value only had three significant figures). In this case, it makes sense to keep the number of **decimal places** the same, since this reflects the resolution of the measuring instrument.

Another example where it makes sense to consider decimal places rather than the number of significant figures would be in finding the total mass of two objects with masses of 1.24 g and 141.5 g. These values suggest that the first object was measured using a higher resolution instrument (to the nearest 0.01 g) than the second object (to the nearest 0.1 g). When the two values are added together the result should be given to the nearest 0.1 g (the same as for the lower resolution instrument), and so the total mass is written as 142.7 g.

Using judgement when multiplying values

Judgement is also needed in using the rule of thumb when multiplying values. Suppose you are calculating the masses of two blocks of aluminium, of volume 3.6 cm^3 and 4.2 cm^3. Multiplying by the density (2.7 g/cm^3) gives 9.72 g and 11.34 g respectively. All of the starting values have two significant figures, so applying the rule of thumb for the first block means that the calculated value is rounded to 9.7 g. This seems sensible.

However, applying the rule for the second block means rounding the value to 11 g, The only difference between the two calculations is that one gives a result a little under 10 g and the other a little over 10 g, though the first is rounded to the nearest 0.1 g and the second to the nearest 1 g. Here it may be more sensible to round the result for the second block to 11.3 g. Caution is needed to avoid over-rounding in such cases.

Thinking about the purposes of rounding

The above guidance applies to the *final result* of a calculation: in a multi-stage calculation, it is useful to retain *an extra significant figure* for the *intermediate values* that are calculated, in order to avoid rounding errors accumulating. On the other hand, rounding values to just *one significant figure* can be helpful if they are being used in a calculation to give an order of magnitude estimate.

Summary

There are no hard-and-fast rules for deciding on an appropriate number of significant figures. One difficulty is that this is linked to measurement uncertainty – a complex and subtle idea. However, that does not mean that 'anything goes', and the above discussion indicates some of the considerations for making sensible choices.

It is important that pupils should be able to identify the number of significant figures in a value, and to know how to round to a given number of significant figures. This is a matter of being correct or incorrect. Assessing how well they can round to appropriate numbers of significant figures involves finding out their reasons for doing so.

2.4 Calculating means

The **mean** of a set of values is the *sum* of the values divided by the *number* of values. (Strictly speaking, this is called the **arithmetic mean**, to distinguish it from other means such as the *geometric mean*.) The arithmetic mean is so widely used that, in science, it is usually referred to as just the 'mean'. A common situation in school science for finding a mean is when taking repeated measurements in an experiment. The use of the term 'average' as an alternative to 'mean' should be avoided, since 'average' can be ambiguous. (See Section 6.5 *How big is a typical value?* on page 55 for further details about means and averages.)

The same considerations about significant figures apply to the calculation of means. For example, using the 'rule of thumb' when calculating the mean of the three measured values 7.5 cm, 7.8 cm and 7.6 cm gives a result of 7.6 cm. The sum of these numbers divided by 3 is 7.633 333, and the final result is given to *two* significant figures, since the original values have *two* significant figures. Note that the value '3' is an integer, and is *exactly* 3, so it is not treated as having one significant figure.

For a larger number of values, it may be justified for a mean to have a greater number of significant figures than the values of the data. For example, suppose you have 10 grapes and a balance reading to the nearest 1 g. The best way of finding the mean would be to put them all on the balance to get a total mass and divide by 10. But suppose instead that the mass of each grape is measured individually: 6 g, 5 g, 6 g, 7 g, 5 g, 5 g, 6 g, 6 g, 5 g and 6 g. The total is 57 g, and the mean would be 5.7 g.

Here it may be better *not* to round to 6 g, but to leave it as 5.7 g. The full explanation for this involves thinking about the possible range for the true value. Since the balance reads to the nearest 1 g, each measured value could be higher or lower than the true value by up to 0.5 g (e.g. a reading of 5 g means the true value is closer to this than to 4 g or 6 g, and lies between 4.5 g and 5.5 g). It is possible, though unlikely, that *all* the random measurement effects were working in the *same direction*. If all 10 measurements were too high, their total could be *higher* than the true value of the total by a maximum of 5 g (i.e. 10×0.5 g); if they were all too low, their total could be *lower* than the true value by a maximum of 5 g. Thus the true value of the total lies between 52 g and 62 g. These extremes, however, are very unlikely. It is much more probable that there will be some cancelling out of these random effects, with 57 g being the *best guess* of the total mass.

Another example of finding a mean is given in Section 6.2 *Variability and measurement uncertainty* on page 51, where the calculated value is rounded to *fewer* significant figures than the measured values, because there is a good deal of variability in the measurements.

These examples illustrate the difficulty in 11–16 science of providing hard-and-fast rules or full justifications for how to round to appropriate numbers of significant figures; it is best left to judgements about what seems to make good sense.

2.5 Index notation and powers

Pupils are most likely to come across **index notation** for the first time in the context of expressing the **square** of a number, for example that 3×3 can be expressed as 3^2 (and spoken as '3 squared'). In this example, the number '2' is called the **index** (or **power** or **exponent**), and, in speech, the expression can also be read as '3 to the *power* of 2'. This can be extended to the **cube** of a number (e.g. 3^3, '3 cubed' or '3 to the power of 3') and to higher indices (e.g. 3^4, 3^5, 3^6, etc.).

The use of indices also applies to *units*. For example, the area of a piece of paper of size 20 cm by 10 cm can be expressed in units of cm^2.

$$\text{area of paper} = 20\,cm \times 10\,cm = 20 \times 10 \times cm \times cm = 200\,cm^2$$

Note that the unit is better pronounced 'square centimetres' rather than 'centimetres squared'. Saying '200 square centimetres' is unambiguous and gives a more direct sense of the area: saying '200 centimetres squared' could be interpreted as either $200\,cm^2$ or $(200\,cm)^2$, i.e. as $40\,000\,cm^2$. Other common units used in science involving indices are m^2 ('square metres'), cm^3 ('cubic centimetres'), dm^3 ('cubic decimetres') and m^3 ('cubic metres').

The symbol $\sqrt{}$ is used for the **square root** of a number. For example, the square root of 9 can be written as $\sqrt{9}$. This has two values, 3 and -3 (also written as ± 3), since both 3^2 and $(-3)^2$ are equal to 9. Similarly, the symbol for a **cube root** is $\sqrt[3]{}$, so $\sqrt[3]{27} = 3$. (Note that 27 has only one cube root, since $(-3)^3$ is -27 and not 27).

Roots may also be expressed using *fractional indices*, so the square root of 9 would be written as $9^{1/2}$, the cube root of 27 would be written as $27^{1/3}$, and so on. In science, the use of fractional indices may be encountered post-16, though it is not common at secondary level. The notion of a fractional index might seem odd at first: while 3^2 can be explained as meaning 3×3, what could $3^{1/2}$ mean? One way of thinking about this is to consider what happens to indices in multiplication. For example, $3^2 \times 3^3 = 3^5$ ($3 \times 3 \times 3 \times 3 \times 3$); the two indices are added together. In a similar way, $3^{1/2} \times 3^{1/2} = 3^1$ (i.e. 3). So, $3^{1/2}$ is the number which when multiplied by itself gives 3; in other words, it is the square root of 3.

The **reciprocal** of a number can also be represented using index notation. For example, the reciprocal of 2 is ½, which can also be written as 2^{-1}. Similarly, the reciprocal of 2^2 (i.e. the reciprocal of 4, which is ¼) can be represented as 2^{-2}. Again, negative indices are not commonly used in secondary school science, except for powers of 10 as described below. Post-16 students would be expected to be familiar with the scientific convention of using negative indices in units, such as for velocity ($m\,s^{-1}$) or density ($g\,cm^{-3}$), but for younger pupils in science it is clearer if these are expressed as m/s or g/cm^3.

Like fractional indices, negative indices can also seem strange. Here, thinking about what happens during division can help. For example, $100\,000 \div 1000 = 100$ can be written as $10^5 \div 10^3 = 10^2$. Here the second index is subtracted from the first. Similarly, $1000 \div 100\,000 = \frac{1}{100}$ can be written as $10^3 \div 10^5 = 10^{-2}$.

2.6 Dealing with very large and very small values

The standard unit of length is the metre but lengths that are much larger or much smaller may be better expressed in different units using **unit prefixes**. For example:

- the thickness of a coin (0.0015 m) is more clearly expressed in millimetres (1.5 mm)
- the distance between two towns (135 000 m) is more clearly expressed in kilometres (135 km).

This avoids having too many zeros, either before or after the decimal point. Large numbers can be written by leaving a space (not a comma) between every three digits, which makes them easier to read, though still not as clear as changing units.

In the SI system, there are unit prefixes covering a wide range of sizes, creating a 'ladder' with each step differing from the next by a factor of 1000 (or 10^3). Figure 2 shows the most commonly used unit prefixes.

Figure 2.1 Prefixes for SI units

Unit prefix	Unit prefix symbol	Multiplying factor		Example	
				Unit name	Unit symbol
tera-	T	1 000 000 000 000	or 10^{12}	terawatt	TW
giga-	G	1 000 000 000	or 10^9	gigawatt	GW
mega-	M	1 000 000	or 10^6	megawatt	MW
kilo-	k	1 000	or 10^3	kilowatt	kW
–	–	1	or 10^0	watt	W
milli-	m	0.001	or 10^{-3}	milliwatt	mW
micro-	μ	0.000 001	or 10^{-6}	microwatt	μW
nano-	n	0.000 000 001	or 10^{-9}	nanowatt	nW

In addition, two other prefixes are centi- (a hundredth) and deci- (a tenth), though these are only likely to be met as the centimetre (1 cm = 0.01 m) and the cubic decimetre (1 dm^3 = 0.001 m^3 = 1000 cm^3).

Changing units can also help in comparing the sizes of values. For example, it is not easy to compare the masses of two objects expressed as 417 g and 1.24 kg. If they are both expressed in the same units, as 417 g and 1240 g, it may be easier to see that the second mass is about three times the first.

It is a common misconception that 'longer' numbers are bigger – the rule works for integers, but pupils may apply this inappropriately to any number. For example, when given the masses of two objects as 0.317 g and 0.52 g, pupils may think the first value is bigger ('317' is bigger than '52'). Converting the values to 317 mg and 520 mg makes the relative size clearer.

Another way of expressing very large or small values is to use **standard form** (also referred to as **standard index form** or **scientific notation**). For example:

127 000 in standard form becomes 1.27×10^5

In standard form, the first number has just one digit to the left of the decimal point (i.e. it is greater than or equal to 1 and less than 10); this is multiplied by a **power of 10**.

One advantage of standard form is that it can make it easier to compare the **orders of magnitude** of very large or very small values. For example, 5.18×10^8 seconds is about 100 times bigger than 5.91×10^6 seconds. Written in full, the eye would be distracted by all the zeros; unless they were arranged one above the other, it would be hard to make the comparison. However, in order to make comparisons using standard form, pupils do need to be confident in using the notation. If they are not then comparison may be easier with the the numbers written in full.

Another advantage of using standard form is that it always makes clear the number of significant figures. An example given earlier was the problem of knowing the number of significant figures in the value 6300 m, and how this can be made clear by changing the units. Expressing in standard form is another way of showing this; for example, as 6.3×10^3 m (two significant figures) or 6.300×10^3 m (four significant figures).

It can also be easier to do calculations using standard form; for example, in multiplying 3.7×10^4 by 1.81×10^7. A calculator can be used to multiply 3.7 by 1.81 to give 6.697. Multiplying the powers of 10 can then be done mentally ($10^4 \times 10^7 = 10^{11}$) to give a final answer of 6.697×10^{11}. Using the numbers written in full on a calculator could easily lead to mistakes being made.

Multiplying 3.7×10^4 by 7×10^7 in the same way gives 25.9×10^{11} but this result is not in standard form, since 25.9 is greater than 10. When expressed in standard form, the result is 2.59×10^{12}.

Adding and subtracting numbers in standard form is trickier. The easiest way is to express them as 'ordinary numbers' and then carry out the calculation. The result can then be changed back to standard form.

Note that, when writing large numbers, it is now generally preferred in science to use a space rather than a comma as a 'thousand separator', i.e. to write 50 000 rather than 50,000. No separator is needed for numbers less than 10 000, i.e. 5000 rather than 5 000. The comma, however, is still the norm for everyday use in the UK. In many other countries, the comma has a different meaning: it is used as the 'decimal mark' instead of the dot used in the UK (e.g. 13,63 instead of 13.63).

2.7   Approximations and orders of magnitude

It is a useful habit when doing calculations to ask 'Does this make sense?' There are two things to consider – one is about the process of calculation and the other is about the 'real-world' values produced.

In both science and mathematics, pupils should be encouraged to use **approximations** so that they can check, for example, that when they use a calculator the output is roughly what they expect. They can do this by rounding all of the numbers in a calculation to one significant figure. For example, if the calculation is to multiply 36.9 by 6.2 then this becomes $40 \times 6 = 240$. The actual result is 228.78, which is close to the **estimate**, but if they get 22 878 then they know that something has gone wrong. This number is the wrong **order of magnitude**.

It is also important to think about whether a calculated value makes sense as an order of magnitude related to the real world; for example, a leaf of mass 3.97 kg, a temperature rise of water of 250 °C, or a car travelling down a motorway at 90 metres per hour. The first two values are far too large and the third is far too small. Being able to make such judgements requires pupils to have a sense of the magnitude of a range of units. Such an understanding can start early, for example with units of mass and length related to familiar objects, extending later to a wider range of values and to other quantities such as energy and power.

3 Choosing how to represent data

> **Key words:** variable, unit, raw data, categorical, discrete, continuous, factor, frequency, frequency table, grouped data, two-way table, pie chart, bar chart, grouped bar chart, stacked bar chart, independent variable, dependent variable, data point, horizontal axis, vertical axis, line graph, gradient, time series, scatter graph.

Tables, charts and graphs are all ways of representing data, and they can be used for two broad purposes. The first is to support the collection, organisation and analysis of data as part of the process of a scientific study. The second is to help present the conclusions of a study to a wider audience. The choices of how to represent data are influenced by:

- the nature of the data
- the kinds of questions about the data that are of interest.

3.1 Using tables to collect and present data

When constructing a table of data, one consideration is what to put in the rows and what to put in the columns. A common form of data in science involves two related *variables*, for example the temperature of a cooling object against time (Figure 3.1).

Figure 3.1 Temperature of a cooling object

(a)

Time (s)	Temperature (°C)
0	59.5
30	54.3
60	51.2
90	48.4
etc.	

(b)

Time (s)	0	30	60	90	etc.
Temperature (°C)	59.5	54.3	51.2	48.4	

The reason that the table in Figure 3.1a works better for collecting data is because it can be easily extended downwards – it is not so easy to extend Figure 3.1b. However, it also has the advantage that, by aligning the values for each quantity vertically, it is easier for the eye to scan down and compare the sizes of values. This is harder to do when the eye has to scan across a horizontal arrangement of values. When making tables intended for *presenting* data, this is a particular consideration, and more complex tables may require careful thought.

The *units* of the values are included at the top of the column along with the variable name, so that the rest of the table just shows the *numbers*. Note that the units are enclosed in *brackets*, for example 'Temperature (°C)'. This is the most usual convention in secondary school science and mathematics for the column headers in tables of data and for labelling axes on graphs. Another convention is to write 'Temperature in °C'. In scientific literature and in post-16 studies, a common convention is to use the '/' symbol (the *solidus*, or forward slash), for example 'Temperature/°C)'. This is intended to indicate that the values of temperature are divided by the unit °C to produce 'pure numbers'. This is a subtle idea, which is why brackets are more suitable for secondary science. In addition, pupils need to be familiar with the 'brackets' convention, since it is widely used on tables and charts intended for a general audience, including those produced by scientific organisations.

Since pupils may come across graphs using different conventions from a variety of sources (in books, on the internet and so on), teachers may wish their pupils to be familiar with all of them. In any case, it is important to check which convention they will meet in their examinations.

Care should be taken, however, if the pupils are not familiar with the use of negative indices in units, which is also usually not introduced until post-16 (see Section 2.5 *Index notation and powers* on page 19). Thus, while both 'velocity (m/s)' and 'velocity/m s^{-1}' are acceptable and considered to be correct, 'velocity/m/s' is ambiguous and confusing and it should thus be avoided.

3.2 Using tables to process data

Tables are also used to support the processing of **raw data** in various ways. One example is when further columns are added to a table to carry out calculations on existing columns. Figure 3.2 shows a table in which two of the columns (Mass and Volume) are used to collect measured values, while the final column (Density) contains calculated values.

Figure 3.2 Calculating density from mass and volume

Another example is when raw data from one table are *counted* to produce further tables showing the values of the counts. For example, in a survey of the pupils in a class, counting the raw data on eye colour (Figure 3.3a) produces a 'table of counts' (Figure 3.3b). Such a table is called a **frequency table**. In mathematics, a **frequency** refers to the number obtained by counting objects or events. Thus, if there are 7 pupils with eye colour 'blue' then this category has a frequency of 7.

The column 'Eye colour' in Figure 3.3a contains **categorical** data. The raw data in this table also include 'shoe sizes', and these are **discrete** data. It would also be possible to count the number of pupils with each shoe size but there might be quite a large number of categories. Here, it may be more convenient to use fewer categories, by choosing some *groups of shoe sizes*, and to count the numbers in these. Figure 3.3c is also a frequency table but here is showing **grouped data**.

It is also possible to create groups from **continuous** data; this is discussed in Section 6.4 *Displaying larger sets of values* on page 53.

Figure 3.3 Survey of pupils in a class

(a) Table of raw data

Pupil	Eye colour	Shoe size
1	brown	1½
2	blue	5
3	brown	5½
4	brown	4
etc.		

(b) Frequency table

Eye colour	Number of pupils
Blue	
Brown	
Green	

(c) Frequency table (grouped data)

Shoe size	Number of pupils
2½ or less	
3 to 5	
5½ or more	

(d) Two-way table

Eye colour	Shoe size		
	2½ or less	3 to 5	5½ or more
Blue			
Brown			
Green			

The tables in Figure 3.3b and 3.3c each show the numbers of pupils categorised by one independent variable or **factor** (eye colour or shoe size).

The table in Figure 3.3d shows the numbers of pupils categorised by *both of these factors*. This is also a frequency table, and is called a **two-way table**. Such tables are useful to see if two factors are related – for example, if there were a large number of pupils with green eyes and large shoe sizes, then this might suggest a relationship between the two factors (though perhaps unlikely in this example).

3.3 Presenting data visually

The most common types of charts and graphs for presenting data are **pie charts**, **bar charts**, **line graphs** and **scatter graphs**. As with tables, visual displays of data can be useful both in the analysis of data and in the presentation of the results.

Displaying data visually can be particularly useful in *comparing the relative sizes of values* and in *looking for relationships between variables*. Visual displays are less useful in communicating actual values: people tend to focus on the patterns rather than the numbers. To emphasise actual values, a table is more effective.

Choosing what charts or graphs to draw is influenced by the nature of the data. The rest of this section will look at the different kinds of display that can be used to represent the following commonly found data structures:

- *A quantity categorised by one factor*
  (e.g. numbers of people in a sample categorised by eye colour)
- *A quantity categorised by two factors*
  (e.g. UK energy consumption categorised by type of fuel and year)
- *Two related quantities*
  (e.g. the extension of a spring related to the mass suspended from it).

Another type of data is simply a set of values for a single quantity (e.g. the heights of a sample of pupils). The analysis of this kind of data and the displays used (*histograms* and *boxplots*) are discussed later. (See Chapter 6 *Dealing with variability* on page 50 and Chapter 8 *Looking for relationships: batches and scatter graphs* on page 75.)

3.4 Charts showing a quantity categorised by one factor

Figure 3.4a shows a quantity (number of people in a sample) categorised by one *factor* (eye colour). Because it is meaningful to add these values to give a *total*, one possible display is a *pie chart* (Figure 3.4b).

An advantage of a pie chart is that it helps to show the size of each category relative to the whole (the category 'green eyes' represents nearly a quarter of the sample), but it is not always easy to compare the sizes of the sectors to each other (the sizes of 'blue' and 'brown' look very similar). Although pie charts are often found in everyday media reports, they are not much used in scientific publications. In mathematics, pupils construct their own pie charts and consider how they are used by others: constructing a pie chart draws on and develops a number of ideas, including data handling, working out percentages and doing calculations on angles.

Another possibility is a *bar chart* (Figure 3.4c). Here, it is much easier to compare the sizes of the three values ('blue' is a bit bigger than 'brown', and nearly twice as much as 'green'). However, now it is harder to judge the fractional size of each category compared with the whole.

The choice of whether to use a *pie chart* or a *bar chart* depends on whether the focus is on the sizes of the categories relative to the whole or relative to each other.

Figure 3.4 Eye colours of a sample of people

(a) Table of data

Eye colour	Number
Blue	63
Brown	58
Green	35
Total	**156**

(c) Bar chart

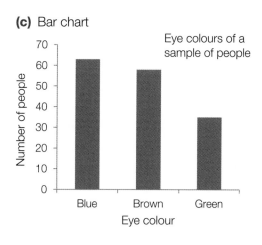

(b) Pie chart

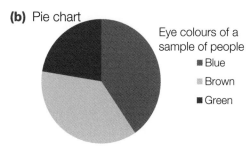

Figure 3.5 also shows a quantity (temperature) categorised by one factor (colour of surface). In this case, it is not meaningful to add these values to give a total. A pie chart would not make sense, so only a bar chart is possible.

Figure 3.5 Temperatures of different coloured surfaces exposed to sunlight

Surface colour	Temperature (°C)
White	24.6
Grey	39.3
Black	43.5

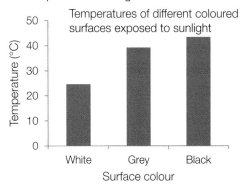

In this example, it is not meaningful to compare the *ratios* of the values since the Celsius temperature scale has an arbitrary zero (i.e. it does not make sense to say that the value for 'black' is nearly twice as big as that for 'white'). However, comparing the heights of the bars does make it possible to compare the *differences* in temperature.

3.5 Charts showing a quantity categorised by two factors

Figure 3.6 shows a quantity (UK annual energy consumption) categorised by two **factors** (type of fuel and year). Here it is meaningful to add the values for the types of fuel together to give the total energy consumption for a year but it is *not* useful to add the values for each year together. There are a variety of different types of display that could be drawn for these data, as illustrated in Figure 3.7.

Figure 3.6 UK annual energy consumption

Million tonnes of oil equivalent (mtoe)		
	1975	2005
Solid fuel	73.7	39.9
Petroleum	85.0	78.2
Gas	35.1	94.3
Bioenergy and waste	0	4.2
Primary electricity*	8.5	19.8
Total	202.3	236.4

* from nuclear, hydro, wind, solar

Figure 3.7a shows two **pie charts**, one for each year, and drawn to the same size. As with a single pie chart, the focus is on comparisons of the parts with the whole for each year; however, it is not easy to compare the two to see how the proportions have changed from one year to the next. To represent the *actual* sizes of the values, the two pie charts could be drawn with *different* sizes, the area of each whole pie representing the value of the total. However, it can be very difficult to judge the relative sizes of segments from different sized pies and with different angles. In general, using multiple pie charts to make comparisons is often not very effective.

Multiple pie charts are rarely used in scientific publications. However, in mathematics lessons, drawing pie charts of different sizes can be a helpful way for pupils to think about how the sizes of the values depend on both the size and the fraction of the total.

There are a number of choices of **bar chart** when the quantity is categorised by two factors. Figures 3.7b and 3.7c are both examples of a **grouped bar chart** (also known as a *clustered*

Figure 3.7 A variety of charts showing UK annual energy consumption

(a) Pie charts

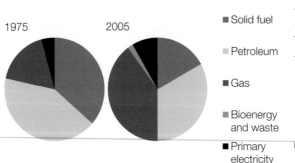

(b) Grouped bar chart 1

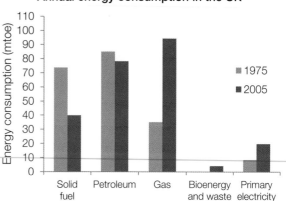

(c) Grouped bar chart 2

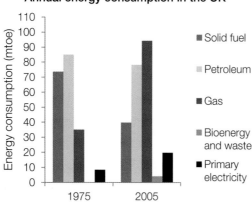

(d) Stacked bar chart 1

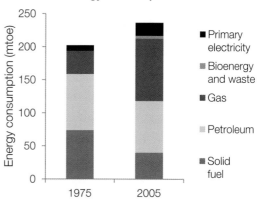

(e) Stacked bar chart 2

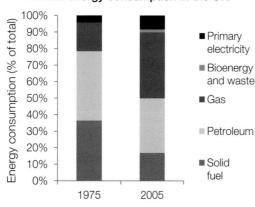

(f) Horizontal bar chart

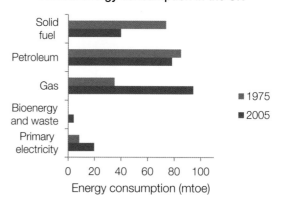

bar chart). By showing a 'profile' for each year, Figure 3.7b makes it easier to compare the contributions of different fuels within each year, but harder to look at the change for each fuel over this period. By contrast, Figure 3.7c emphasises the change for each fuel over the period, but it is not as easy to see the contributions within a single year. The choice of which chart to draw depends on what comparison is of more interest.

Since the values for each type of fuel can be added to give a total, it is possible to draw a **stacked bar chart** (also known as *compound bar chart*). Two forms of the chart are shown:

one where the total height of each bar corresponds to the total quantity (Figure 3.7d) and the other where the values are expressed as percentages and the total height of each bar represents 100% (Figure 3.7e). Since the total energy consumption for each year is fairly similar, in this case the two charts are not very different from each other. In a sense, a stacked bar chart is a compromise between a pie chart and a grouped bar chart. It allows the sizes of parts to be compared with the whole (though not as easily as in a pie chart) and the parts to be compared with each other (though not as easily as in a grouped bar chart). This technique can also be applied to line graphs to show a number of different quantities (a *stacked line graph*), but these are often hard to interpret.

Finally, although all of the bar charts shown so far have been drawn with vertical bars, any type can be drawn with horizontal bars, for example as in Figure 3.7f. The eye may sometimes find it easier to make comparisons of bars by looking down a chart (in the same way that it is easier to compare numbers when written in a column).

3.6   Line graphs and scatter graphs: two related quantities

The tables of data in Figures 3.8, 3.9 and 3.10 all have data about two related quantities. There are a number of *similarities* between these three sets of data and the way they can be displayed, but also some important *differences*.

All of the examples can be thought of as showing a **dependent variable** plotted against an **independent variable**:

- *outside temperature* against *time*
  (time is normally considered as the independent variable)
- *extension of a spring* against *mass added*
  (the mass added is the independent variable, since this is what is being changed in the experiment)
- *mean lifespan for mammals* against *mean heart rate*
  (here, the hypothesis is being tested that heart rate affects lifespan, so heart rate is being treated as the independent variable).

For each value of the independent variable, there is a corresponding value of the dependent variable. These values are used to plot a series of **data points** on a graph; the independent variable has been plotted along the **horizontal axis** and the dependent variable along the **vertical axis**.

So far, all three sets of data have been treated the same – the differences arise when deciding whether to draw a line and how to draw it.

Figure 3.8 shows an example of a **line graph**. It shows the change in outside temperature over a 24-hour period. Lines have been drawn *connecting each data point to the next one*. The assumption being made here is that each value for outside temperature is the *actual value for that particular time and place*, and so the line that is drawn passes through *all* the points. This example is a **time series**, and the graph shows the variation of a quantity over time (a *trend*). The **gradient** of each line segment gives an indication of how quickly the quantity changes from one value to the next. For example, the temperature changed more slowly over the first 3-hour period than over the second.

Figure 3.8 Outside temperature over a 24-hour period starting at midnight

Time (hours)	Outside temperature (°C)
0	8.7
3	9.1
6	13.6
9	15.9
12	19.2
15	21.1
18	14.9
21	12.0
24	10.1

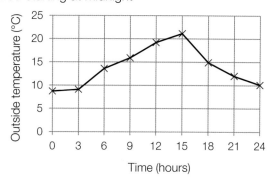

Care needs to be taken, however, in thinking about what happens between the measured values. Although the dependent variable (temperature) varies continuously throughout, and lines are used to connect the data points, these lines are *not* intended to indicate how the dependent variable changes between the data points.

The graph in Figure 3.9 is also an example of a **line graph**. It shows how the extension of a spring depends on the mass suspended from it. Here, instead of connecting all the points together, a single straight line has been drawn that passes as close as possible to the points (though not necessarily through them), called a *line of best fit*. This type of line graph is very common in science. The assumption here is that there is a simple relationship between the two variables such that the *true values* all lie on the line: if all of the values could be measured with complete accuracy then every value of mass added would have a value of the extension of the spring that would lie on the line. In practice, not all the data points fit on this line because of *measurement uncertainties*.

Figure 3.9 Effect of adding slotted masses to a spring

Mass added (g)	Extension (mm)
0	0
100	24
200	45
300	66
400	98
500	112
600	133
700	154
800	178

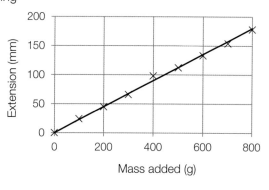

Unlike the previous type of line graph (in Figure 3.8), a fitted line *is* intended to indicate how the dependent variable changes between the data points. (For further details, see Section 7.5 *Interpolation and extrapolation on a line graph* on page 70).

In both Figure 3.8 and Figure 3.9, the nature of the data suggests that for every value of the independent variable there will be a *single value* for the dependent variable. This is the justification for drawing a line to represent the relationship between the variables.

This is in contrast to the data in Figure 3.10, which shows the relationship between mean heart rate and mean lifespan for various types of mammal. This is a **scatter graph** and no line has been drawn since the data are of a different type to the previous example involving the spring. The pattern of data points suggests that mammals with a higher heart rate (and higher metabolic rate) tend to have shorter lifespans. In this example, it is easy to imagine that there might be two types of mammal with the same mean heart rate but different lifespans (i.e. the same values for the independent variable but different values for the dependent variable). Unlike the example about the spring (Figure 3.9), there is not a unique value of the dependent variable for every value of the independent variable. A line thus cannot be drawn that passes *through or close to all the points.*

Figure 3.10 Mean heart rates and lifespans for some selected types of mammal

Mammal	Heart rate (beats/min)	Lifespan (years)
Badger	138	11
Cat	120	15
Elephant	35	24
Goat	90	9
Hamster	450	1.5
Horse	44	25
Mouse	600	2
Rabbit	205	5.5
Rat	328	2.5
Squirrel	354	9

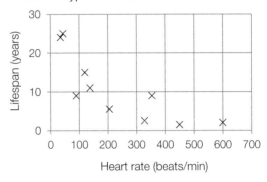

Since there does appear to be some kind of relationship between these two variables, it would be possible to draw a fitted line. The pattern of data points on the graph suggests that a curve would be a better fit than a straight line. This curve would have a different meaning to the line in Figure 3.9. Most of the data points would not be close to the fitted curve, and this would not be due to *measurement uncertainty* but to the *variability between different types of mammal.*

Note that, in mathematics, when pupils encounter 'line graph' it is usually of the type shown in Figure 3.8, and they would talk of connecting each pair of data points with a 'line segment'. In science, 'line graphs' of the type shown in Figure 3.9 are more common. When pupils draw a line of best fit in mathematics, it is more likely to be for the type of data shown in Figure 3.10 (a 'scatter graph') rather than for that shown in Figure 3.9, and the fitted line would be straight. In science lessons, pupils are expected to judge whether a line of fit should be straight or curved. (See Section 8.8 *Drawing a line of best fit on a scatter graph* on page 85.)

Care in using terminology also needs to be taken when drawing a line graph or a scatter graph with a computer spreadsheet, such as *Excel*. For example, in drawing a line graph such as that in Figure 3.9, the spreadsheet needs to have two columns of data, with values of mass and extension. Selecting these and choosing a 'line graph' option produces two lines – one for each variable plotted sequentially. Confusingly, whenever you want to plot one variable against another, a 'scatter graph' option needs to be selected, whether you want to draw a line on the graph or not.

Sometimes it can seem that different sciences have different ways of handling data. The important point made in this section is that *different types of data* are handled in different ways. Since biology, chemistry and physics are often concerned with different types of data, each subject has different emphases on how to handle such data. Experiments involving a relationship between two continuous variables are found across the sciences but are a particular focus in physics. Such experiments lead to *'line graph' type data*. Surveys involving data collection from individuals in a population are more common in biology than other subjects and lead to *'scatter graph' type data*.

The distinction between these two fundamentally different kinds of data is very important. How such data are analysed is discussed in more detail in the following two chapters:

- Chapter 7 *Looking for relationships: line graphs* on page 64
- Chapter 8 *Looking for relationships: batches and scatter graphs* on page 75.

3.7 Bar charts and line graphs

Examples of **bar charts** and **line graphs** have been discussed earlier. The bar chart shown in Figure 3.5 has a horizontal axis that represents a **categorical** variable. The line graph shown in Figure 3.9 has a horizontal axis that represents a **continuous** variable. But what about data where the independent variable is a **discrete** variable? Is a bar chart or a line graph better for this kind of data? This is a question that can generate a good deal of disagreement. (See Section 1.4 *Naming different types of data* on page 12 for further details about the meanings of these terms, in particular the discussion about the similarities between continuous and discrete data.)

Figure 3.11 is an example of data that has a *discrete* independent variable. It shows the voltage measured across a number of batteries (or 'cells') connected in series. (The ones used were in fact standard D-size alkaline cells marked '1.5 V'.)

Figure 3.11 Voltage across cells connected in series

Number of cells	Voltage (V)
1	1.55
2	3.11
3	4.66
4	6.22
5	7.78
6	9.33

The independent variable here is 'number of cells' – it is a *discrete* variable. A discrete variable has similarities to both a *continuous* variable and a *categorical* variable:

- It is similar to a *continuous* variable in that they are both numerical (the numbers are related to the sizes of the values).

- It is similar to a *categorical* variable in that there are no 'in-between' values (e.g. '1½ cells' has no meaning).

If 'number of cells' is treated as being more similar to a *categorical* variable then a *bar chart* would be plotted, as shown in Figure 3.12a; if it is treated as being more similar to a *continuous* variable then a *line graph* would be plotted, as shown in Figure 3.12b.

Figure 3.12 Bar chart and line graph of the same data

(a) Bar chart

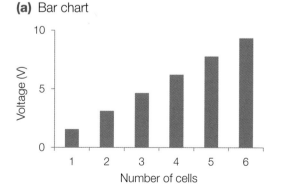

(b) Line graph

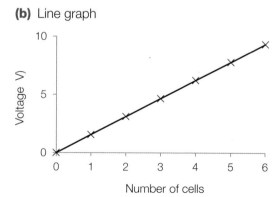

One of the arguments used for saying that a bar chart should be drawn for data like these is that it is not meaningful to draw a line when the values on the horizontal axis are discrete. This is because there are no 'in-between' values for the number of cells, and **interpolation** would not make sense (see Section 7.5 *Interpolation and extrapolation on a line graph* on page 70). For example, it is possible to read from the graph that to get a voltage of 5 V you would need about 3¼ cells – and you can't have 3¼ cells.

The problem with this argument is that, although there is nothing to stop anyone trying to interpolate on a line graph, it is not compulsory. By analogy, the relationship could be represented as an equation:

$$\text{voltage} = \text{number of cells} \times 1.55\,\text{V}$$

There is nothing here to indicate that 'number of cells' is a discrete variable and that only integer values could be substituted. In the same way, if we draw a line graph then we can use our judgement to decide on those aspects of the representation that may be useful (e.g. the gradient of the line) and those that may not (e.g. interpolation).

If there are only two values (for 1 and 2 cells) then a bar chart would certainly be better, since there are too few data points to draw a line. However, with a sufficient number of values, a line graph has many advantages.

- *Seeing patterns*: It is easier to see whether the points lie on a straight line or a curve, and to identify how close the measurements are to the fitted line.

- *Interpreting gradients*: It is possible to calculate the gradient of the line, and to obtain an equation for the relationship. The gradient is meaningful here because the numerical differences between values on the horizontal axis are meaningful (it is an *interval scale*).

- *Interpolating*: Although interpolation may not be meaningful if *all* of the discrete values have been measured, it does makes sense if there are 'missing' values. For example, if there are voltages for 1, 2, 5, 10, 15 and 20 cells then interpolation could be used to estimate voltages for other numbers of cells.

- *Extrapolating*: The line can be extrapolated to estimate values beyond the measured range.

- *Dealing with 'missing values'*: On a bar chart it may be difficult to represent discrete data consisting of a small number of values spread across a wide range. For example, suppose there are only five values corresponding to 5, 25, 50, 100 and 200 on the horizontal axis. One could either show these as equally spaced bars and lose the visual appearance of the relationship or show the whole scale from 1, 2, 3 ... 200, creating five narrow bars and a lot of spaces. Plotting a line graph would show the relationship more clearly. When the values of a discrete variable become very large (e.g. populations of countries), it certainly makes sense to treat these in the same way as continuous variables.

- *Meaningful non-integer values*: It is not possible to have, say, 2.5 rubber bands but, in an experiment involving forces related to rubber bands, interpolation may be meaningful. 'Number of rubber bands' becomes in effect a 'surrogate' unit of force, which is a continuous variable.

Line graphs of discrete data can also be useful when lines are used to join each data point to the next one. Such graphs are used to plot the properties of elements (e.g. their melting points) against atomic number (a discrete variable). Non-integer values of atomic number certainly have no meaning, but a bar chart of these data would be more difficult to interpret.

A line graph emphasises the peaks and the troughs in the data, and makes the periodic patterns stand out.

Sometimes, what appears to be a discrete variable on the horizontal axis actually reflects an underlying continuous variable. For example, 'Monday', 'Tuesday', 'Wednesday', and so on, look like discrete values. However, if the vertical axis represents a person's heart rate recorded at 8.00 am on each day then this really reflects a set of samples along a continuous scale. In principle, the heart rate could have been taken every hour or every minute. Similarly, if the vertical axis represents daily rainfall then this is just a conventional way of recording the total amount of this quantity. Again, in principle, the total could be recorded every hour or every minute. In both of these cases, a line graph could be justified, since the gradients are meaningful.

4   Drawing charts and graphs

> **Key words**: line graph, bar chart, scatter graph, independent variable, dependent variable, time series, axis, horizontal axis, vertical axis, *x*-axis, *y*-axis, origin, range, scale, tick mark, tick mark label, axis label, unit, data point, coordinate, *x*-coordinate, *y*-coordinate.

When drawing a chart or a graph, it is important to think about the purpose of doing this and what kind of display is best for representing the data. This aspect is discussed in the previous chapter (Chapter 3 *Choosing how to represent data*). This chapter focuses on the details of constructing good charts and graphs, and how to make appropriate choices when drawing them by hand on graph paper.

4.1   The important features of a chart or a graph

Line graphs are very common in science. Figure 4.1 shows an example of a line graph that will be used to illustrate its important features but the principles also apply to *bar charts* and *scatter graphs*.

Figure 4.1 An example of a line graph

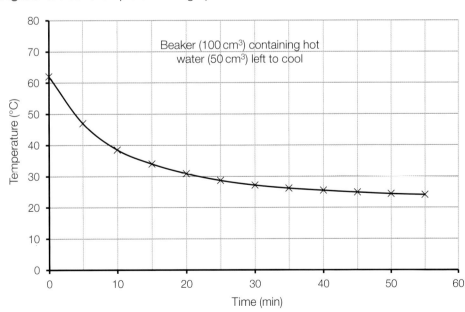

The following is a summary of the points that need to be considered during the construction of a line graph. These are discussed in more detail later in this section.

A graph has two **axes** drawn at right angles: the **horizontal axis** (or **x-axis**) along the bottom and the **vertical axis** (or **y-axis**) up the side.

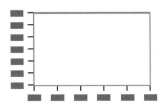

On each axis, there are **tick marks** (the little marks at regular intervals along each axis). There are also **tick mark labels** (the numbers next to the tick marks). Note: for a bar chart, one of the axes (usually the horizontal axis) would have only category labels instead.

Each axis has a label. The **axis label** shows the name of the variable and its unit.

The **data points** are the values plotted on the graph. Each point is plotted using a pair of values for the variables (the **x-coordinate** and the **y-coordinate**). Note: for a bar chart, the bars would be plotted using the data values for each category.

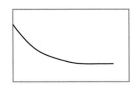

A line is drawn, which either connects all of the data points or is a line of best fit. A scatter graph may show just the data points or it may also have a line of best fit.

Finally, a graph should have a *title* that describes what the graph is showing. If there is more than one line on the graph, there will also need to be a *legend* or *key* to show what each line represents.

4.2 Choosing the axes

A graph shows the relationship between two variables. Usually, the **independent variable** is plotted on the **horizontal axis** or **x-axis** and the **dependent variable** on the **vertical axis** or **y-axis** (Figure 4.2a). Many graphs in science show how something varies over time – a **time series** graph. Here, time is treated as the *independent variable* (Figure 4.2b).

Figure 4.2 Choosing the axes

(a)

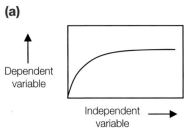

(b)

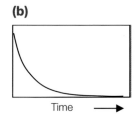

When plotting a graph by hand, another choice is how to orient the graph paper – landscape (wide) or portrait (tall). A landscape graph is nearly always better, especially if there is a lot of variation, as it is easier to identify the gradients. However, a portrait graph might suit rapidly increasing changes, for example exponential growth of bacteria or the rate of a chemical reaction or radioactive decay.

4.3 Choosing the range of each axis

The **range** of the axis refers to the lower and upper limits of the values shown on the axis. It needs to be chosen to cover the **range** of data. (Note that the term 'range' is here being used to refer both to the axis and to the data. Different uses of the term 'range' are explained in the glossary.) For the data shown in Figure 4.1, the values of time vary from 0 to 55 minutes and the temperature varies from about 25 °C to just over 60 °C. One question is whether to include the **origin** (with both axes starting at zero). Many graphs include the origin but not all do. Sometimes the data can be shown more clearly when an axis does not start at zero. For example, Figure 4.3 shows how the shape of a line can be shown more clearly by changing the range of the vertical axis.

Figure 4.3 Choosing whether to include the origin

(a) With origin   **(b)** Without origin

It is possible to find graphs that are similar to Figure 4.3b but which use a convention to show that the range does not start at zero. Such graphs include the zero at the start of the axis but then use a 'squiggly line' or 'zig-zag' to indicate that part of the axis has been 'cut out'. This convention is not used in scientific practice, and should be avoided in school science – the split scale can confuse pupils. When interpreting graphs, though, it is important for pupils to pay attention to the values on the scales and to know whether the graph starts at the origin or not.

Figure 4.3b shows the variation in values more clearly, but the lack of an origin can be misleading. If the *ratios of the values* are meaningful then Figure 4.3a is better for comparing sizes. The striking difference between the shapes of these lines in this example illustrates the importance of identifying the range of each axis when interpreting a line graph.

Note that in Figure 4.1 at the start of this chapter, the origin is included. Although it is not meaningful to compare the relative sizes of temperatures measured in °C, a value of 0 °C is convenient in this case for starting the vertical axis.

Sometimes, the variables plotted on the axes include negative as well as positive values. Examples of such variables include temperatures measured in °C, velocity on a velocity–time graph, or the potential difference across a component. In such cases, the origin would not be plotted at the bottom left of the graph but higher up or to the right or both. Values may be plotted above and below the horizontal axis, and to the left and the right of the vertical axis. An example of such a graph is shown in Chapter 10 (Figure 10.13b, a velocity–time graph for a ball thrown vertically upwards, on page 117).

4.4 Ranges and scales

The **scale** of an axis is how much each square on the graph paper represents. On the graph paper shown, each main division has 10 small squares. A scale must be chosen for each of the axes so that the **range** fits well on the graph paper.

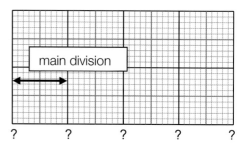

It is helpful if pupils first draw the axes on the graph paper, to ensure that there is sufficient space on the edges of the graph to put labels and values on the axes. They can then see how much space is available for representing the data. (Note that, for simplicity, the edges to the left of and below the axes have not been indicated on the following diagrams.)

Figure 4.4 shows the effect of choosing different scales for the horizontal axis. In Figure 4.4a the scale is appropriate but in Figure 4.4b the data are too squashed and in Figure 4.4c the data do not fit completely on the graph paper.

Figure 4.4 Fitting the range to the graph paper

(a) Appropriate scale

(b) Too squashed

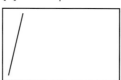

(c) Does not fit

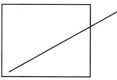

4.5 Choosing a good scale

Pupils find it hard to choose appropriate **scales**. As well as fitting the range to the graph paper, they need to avoid scales that make the values hard to read. A simple rule is that each large square (main division) should have a value of 1, 2 or 5 multiplied by some power of ten. Other values may be suitable, but this rule works well whether the main squares on the graph paper are divided into 5 or 10 sub-divisions. For this rule, each main square should have one of these values:

	0.1	1	10	100	
etc.	0.2	2	20	200	etc.
	0.5	5	50	500	

This makes it easier to work out the values of the small squares. For example, suppose the **range** of values to be plotted on the horizontal axis is from 2 metres to 14 metres. Figure 4.5 shows some possible scales following this rule. Here, the scale in Figure 4.5c would be the best choice.

Figure 4.5 Different scales for plotting the range 2 metres to 14 metres

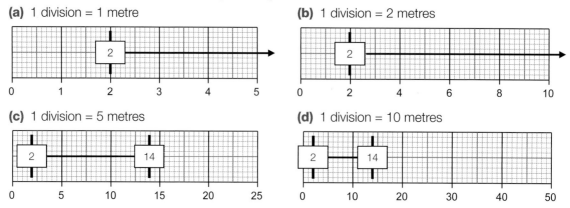

(a) 1 division = 1 metre

(b) 1 division = 2 metres

(c) 1 division = 5 metres

(d) 1 division = 10 metres

In general, the range of the data on each axis should be *over* a half of the space available. A graph with the data points squashed together makes it hard to read accurate values when interpolating or finding a gradient. You can think of the choice of values for each square (e.g. 1, 2, 5, 10, 20, 50) as a ladder where each step is about twice the previous one. If the range of the data occupies less than half the space on an axis, go up the ladder until it does; if it does not fit on the graph paper, go down a step.

Some pupils try to make the data points fill up as much of the space as possible, by choosing values for the scale divisions that are not on this ladder. This is not a good idea; the scale in Figure 4.6 shows an example (1 division = 3 metres). Although the range of values fits well, it is hard to work out what each small square is worth, so plotting the values is not easy and therefore more likely to lead to mistakes.

Figure 4.6 Another scale: 1 division = 3 metres

On a bar chart, the bars are equally spaced along the horizontal axis, and labelled with the values of the independent variable. Sometimes pupils do something similar on a graph, where the values they put on the horizontal scale reflect the data values so that the data points are equally spaced out. It needs to be emphasised to them that on a graph each scale division has the same value. The convention that the values on each axis increase going up and to the right may also need emphasising. Some pupils may try plotting an axis in the opposite direction if the order of the values in a data table seems to them to be in the 'wrong direction'.

4.6 Labels and units

Each axis should include a label that shows the name of the variable and its **unit**, for example 'Time (min)' and 'Temperature (°C)'. The usual convention in secondary school science is for the units to be enclosed in brackets. It is not recommended that the scientific convention of using the '/' symbol (e.g. 'Time/min') be used until post-16 work. (For more details, see Section 3.1 *Using tables to collect and present data* on page 23.)

4.7 Plotting points and finding values

Being able to use the scales on axes is important for two purposes:

- *Plotting points on a graph*: This involves reading a value on each axis and plotting the point where they cross, as in Figure 4.7a. Each **data point** has an **x-coordinate** and **y-coordinate**: the **coordinates** determine the position of the data point in relation to the axes.
- *Reading a value off a line*: Once a line graph has been drawn, it can be used to find values at any point along the line (see Section 7.5 *Interpolation and extrapolation on a line graph* on page 70). This involves finding the value on one axis, seeing where it crosses the line, and then reading the value off the other axis, as in Figure 4.7b.

Figure 4.7 Plotting points and finding values

(a) Plotting a point

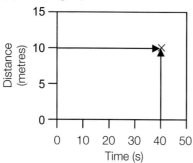

(b) Finding a value

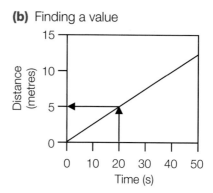

There are no universally accepted conventions for the symbols used to represent data points on graphs. The most common symbol used in school science is ✕, but ⊙ and + are also used. To plot a data point, its position can first be marked with a small dot and then diagonal lines drawn through it to form ✕, or a circle drawn round it to give ⊙. (Note that sometimes drawing a circle around a data point is intended to indicate an outlier.) The advantage of the + symbol is that the position of the point can be found in two stages by drawing first one line and then the other. For older pupils this can lead in to the idea of drawing error bars to indicate uncertainty in the measurements. The disadvantage is that + may not stand out so clearly visually from the gridlines on the graph paper as ✕.

Which symbol (or symbols) to use is really a choice for teachers that depends on the context and what is most appropriate to the pupils. It is a matter of convention not correctness. There is no justification for penalising a pupil for drawing a graph that has 'incorrect' symbols.

4.8 Reading scales

When a data point is on a main division, it is easy to read the value. For example, in Figure 4.8a, the value is 40 seconds. If the data point is not on a main division, it depends on the value of the small squares. In Figure 4.8b, each small square is 1 second, so it is not too difficult to read the value as 16 seconds.

Figure 4.8 Some scales are easier to read than others

(a)

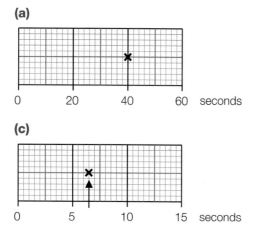

(b)

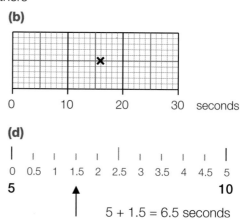

(c)

(d)

The scale in Figure 4.8c is more difficult, since each small square is 0.5 seconds. It may be helpful to jot down the values of the small squares to see how much to add on to the main division (Figure 4.8d). Note that the values for these small squares start at '0'; a common misconception for pupils is that counting always starts at '1'.

5 Working with proportionality and ratio

> **Key words**: proportional, directly proportional, line graph, origin, gradient, slope, horizontal axis, vertical axis, *x*-axis, *y*-axis, *x*-coordinate, *y*-coordinate, rate, constant, constant of proportionality, reciprocal, inverse, inversely proportional, ratio, percentage, scale, scale drawing, scale factor, linear dimension.

There are many different kinds of relationship between variables. A very common relationship is when one variable is *proportional* to another and this section focuses on this kind of relationship. It also considers the related ideas of ratio, percentage and scale.

5.1 Meaning of proportional

A formal way of expressing proportionality would be that variable A is *proportional* to variable B when the values of the two variables are related by a constant multiplier. It is easier to understand the idea of proportionality through an example.

Banks count coins by weighing them. Suppose a coin has a mass of 5 g. Then two coins have a mass of 10 g. Doubling the number of coins doubles the mass. If there are 10 coins then they have 10 times the mass of one coin (i.e. 100 g). This is expressed by saying that the mass of coins is proportional to the number of coins.

A proportional relationship also works the other way round. The number of coins is proportional to the mass of the coins. A bag with 100 g of coins contains 10 coins. If you have double the mass (200 g) then you have double the number of coins (20). This is essentially what the bank is doing when it weighs coins to count them.

5.2 Proportionality and visual representation

Representing a *proportional* relationship as a graph can be a helpful way of exploring the idea further. The example here uses actual results of measuring the mass of a pile of 2p coins, with a reading being taken after each successive coin is added to the pile. The table of results is shown in Figure 5.1a and a *line graph* in Figure 5.1b (the values have been omitted from the graph for simplicity).

There are two key features of a graph showing proportionality between variables:

- the relationship is represented by a *straight line*
- the straight line passes through the *origin*.

Figure 5.1 Measuring the masses of 2p coins

(a)

Number of 2p coins	Total mass (g)
0	0
1	7.12
2	14.24
3	21.36
4	28.48
etc.	

(b)

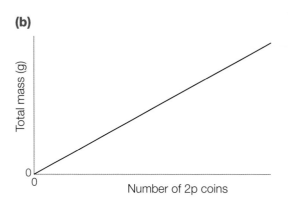

Doubling the numbers of coins doubles the mass (e.g. 4 coins have double the mass of 2 coins, and 6 coins have double the mass of 3 coins). Trebling the number of coins trebles the mass; halving the number of coins halves the mass. Figure 5.2 shows this idea represented on the graph. This is expressed by saying that the mass of the coins is **proportional** to the number of coins. (The term **directly proportional** is also used, but *proportional* is generally the preferred term in science. Using the term 'directly proportional' is helpful when it is being contrasted to 'inversely proportional', as explained later.)

Figure 5.2 Doubling one variable doubles the other

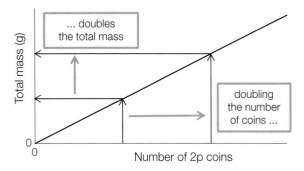

Note that for a relationship to be proportional, the line on the graph needs both to be straight *and* to pass through origin. A curve that passes through the origin does not represent a proportional relationship. A straight line that does not pass through the origin represents a **linear relationship** but not a *proportional* one. A proportional relationship is a special case of a linear relationship. (For more details, see Section 9.11 *Mathematical equations and relationships in science* on page 99.)

Note also that proportionality is not the same as *correlation* – these two terms are sometimes confused with each other. They are both concerned with the relationship between two variables but correlation applies to a different type of data. (See Section 8.7 *Relationships between variables: scatter graphs and correlation* on page 83.)

5.3 Interpretation of gradient

Figure 5.3a shows a graph with *two* lines – now representing the results for measuring the masses of two stacks of coins, of 1p as well as 2p. The line for the 2p coins is *steeper*. This implies that the mass of the 2p stack rises more than the mass of the 1p stack when a coin is added. This is because each 2p coin has a greater mass than a 1p coin. The steepness of the line is called the **gradient** (the term **slope** is also used, but *gradient* is the preferred term).

Figure 5.3 Finding the gradient of a line

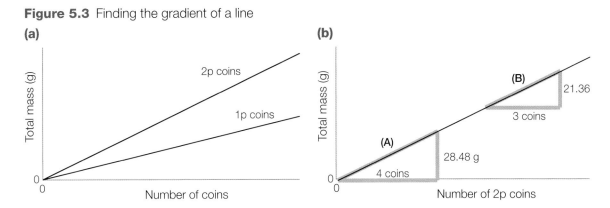

(a)

(b)

Figure 5.3b shows how the gradient of this line can be measured: it is the increase in the variable on the **vertical axis** or **y-axis** divided by the corresponding increase in the variable on the **horizontal axis** or **x-axis**.

Since this is a straight line, it does not matter where this is done or how large the chosen interval is – the gradient is the same along the whole length of the line. For example, in Figure 5.3b, the gradient is measured in two different places along the line. The vertical measure is the difference between the two **y-coordinates**, and the horizontal measure is the difference between the two **x-coordinates**.

$$\text{gradient at (A)} = \frac{28.48 \text{ g}}{4 \text{ coins}} = 7.12 \text{ g per coin}$$

$$\text{gradient at (B)} = \frac{21.36 \text{ g}}{3 \text{ coins}} = 7.12 \text{ g per coin}$$

The gradient works out the same for both (A) and (B), and, in this example, is in fact the mass of one coin.

Note that the two small triangles drawn on this graph are intended only to illustrate that the gradient of this straight line is the same everywhere. When finding the gradient of a line on a real graph of data, the triangle used should be drawn as large as possible (see Section 9.12 *Graphs of quantities against time: gradients* on page 103).

Another example that illustrates the meaning of a gradient is shown in Figure 5.4. The graph shows the change in the volume of water in a bath over time. At the start, the bath is empty. One line represents a fully open tap and the other a tap that is partially closed.

Figure 5.4 A bath filling with water

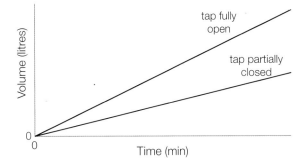

Since this is a change over time, the gradient represents a **rate** of change. In this case, the gradient is the *flow rate* of the water and is measured in litres/min. Both lines are straight and pass through the origin – this is a proportional relationship. For each tap setting, doubling the time will double the volume since the *rate* (i.e. the *gradient*) is constant. The difference in the gradients of the two lines shows that the *rate* of change is greater when the tap is fully open than when it is partially closed.

5.4 Proportionality and algebraic representation

A **proportional** relationship can be represented algebraically as:

variable A $\propto$ variable B

e.g. mass of coins $\propto$ number of coins

The symbol '$\propto$' stands for 'is proportional to'. This relationship can be expressed as a formula:

variable A $=$ constant $\times$ variable B

e.g. mass of coins $=$ mass of one coin $\times$ number of coins

The **constant** in the formula (in this case, 'mass of one coin') is equal to the gradient of the line on the graph. It is called the **constant of proportionality**. The formula has the general form of the mathematical equation:

$$y = kx$$

This represents a straight line passing through the origin with a gradient of k.

Any proportional relationship 'works both ways': so if 'y is proportional to x' then it is also true to say that 'x is proportional to y'. In mathematics, this idea is expressed by saying that 'x and y are in direct proportion'.

A related kind of relationship is when one variable is proportional to the **reciprocal** or **inverse** of another variable, i.e.

$$y \propto \frac{1}{x}$$

This would be described by saying that y is **inversely proportional** to x: if x is doubled then y is halved. The general form of the equation would be:

$$y = \frac{\text{constant}}{x}$$

These ideas about *directly proportional* and *indirectly proportional* relationships are illustrated with some common examples from school science in the next section.

5.5 Proportional relationships in science

Some **proportional** relationships in science arise from *definitions* of quantities and others are derived from *experimental observations*. An example of a definition is:

$$\text{density} = \frac{\text{mass}}{\text{volume}}$$

This is not of the form $y = kx$ but it can be rearranged. (For details on rearranging formulae, see Chapter 9 *Scientific models and mathematical equations* on page 87.)

$$\text{mass} = \text{density} \times \text{volume}$$

For objects made of the same material (i.e. constant density), the mass is proportional to the volume. In Figure 5.5a, the gradient for 'iron' is greater than for 'aluminium' because iron is a more dense material. Here, the **constant of proportionality** is the density of the material and this can be found by calculating the gradient of the straight line.

Figure 5.5 Proportional relationships

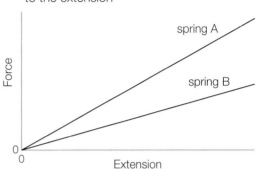

(a) The mass of a particular material is proportional to its volume

(b) The force exerted by a spring is proportional to the extension

An example of a relationship derived from experiment is Hooke's Law. By experiment, it was found that the force exerted by a spring is proportional to the extension (within the elastic limit of the spring). The constant of proportionality is called the spring constant and it is a characteristic of a particular spring: the larger the spring constant, the stiffer the spring (Figure 5.5b).

$$\text{force exerted} = \text{spring constant} \times \text{extension}$$

For each relationship in science, there tends to be a 'conventional' way of expressing the **formula**, and this may not always have the form $y = kx$. The formula may need to be rearranged to express it in this way. In addition, what is considered to be the variable and what is considered to be the constant depends on the context. For example, if bottles of the same fixed volume are each filled with liquids of different densities, the *mass* of the liquid is proportional to the *density* and the *volume* would be the constant.

Figure 5.6 shows selected relationships, with the constants in the formulae underlined.

Figure 5.6 Examples of constants in proportional relationships

Relationship	Formula (constant is underlined)
For an object made of a particular material: mass $\propto$ volume	mass = volume × <u>density</u>
For filling a fixed volume with different liquids: mass $\propto$ density	mass = <u>volume</u> × density
For a car travelling at constant speed along a motorway: distance travelled $\propto$ time	distance travelled = <u>speed</u> × time
For an object moved by a constant force: work done $\propto$ distance	work done = <u>force</u> × distance
For a resistor that obeys Ohm's Law (i.e. a constant resistance): potential difference $\propto$ current	potential difference = current × <u>resistance</u>

Note that saying that something is a *constant* does not mean that it is just a number with no units. In the algebraic equation $y = kx$, the constant of proportionality k does represent just a number. However, in the examples in the above table, all of the constants are values with *units*. Thus, for the first example, mass (g) is proportional to volume (cm^3), and the constant is density (g/cm^3).

Rearranging the kinds of formulae shown in the table above can reveal relationships that are ***inversely proportional***. For example:

$$\text{wave speed} = \text{frequency} \times \text{wavelength}$$

For light in a particular medium, the wave speed is constant. Rearranging the formula brings out more clearly the relationship that frequency is inversely proportional to wavelength.

$$\text{frequency} = \frac{\text{wave speed}}{\text{wavelength}}$$

This means that if the wavelength is *doubled* then the frequency is *halved*. If it is trebled (or multiplied by any amount k) then the frequency is divided by three (or divided by the amount k).

For more details about directly proportional and inversely proportional relationships, see Section 9.11 *Mathematical equations and relationships in science* on page 99.

5.6 Ratios

A ***ratio*** is a comparison of two *similar quantities* and thus does not have units. For example, the mass of a 1p coin is 3.56 g and the mass of a 2p coin is 7.12 g. Thus the ratio of the mass of a 1p coin to the mass of a 2p coin is 3.56 : 7.12 (no units). This reduces to 1 : 2. The mass of a 2p coin is exactly twice that of a 1p coin and so, in this example, the ratio consists of *integers* (whole numbers).

Similarly, in aluminium oxide (Al_2O_3), the ratio of aluminium atoms to oxygen atoms is 2 : 3 – again integers. It is also possible to express this as 1 : 1.5. Which of these ways of expressing a ratio is better is a matter of choice, depending on what is more useful for the context.

The ratio of the width of a sheet of A4 paper (210 mm) to the height (297 mm) is 210 : 297. This is a rather unwieldy ratio. In such cases, the ratio is expressed in the form '1 : x'. For A4 paper, this would be 1 : 1.414. Using a ratio in this form makes comparisons with other ratios easier. For example, the ratio of the width to the height for A3 paper is the same (1 : 1.414) as for A4, showing that the two sizes of paper are similar shapes.

In some ratios, the two quantities being compared are also *parts* of a *whole*. For example, the ratio of aluminium atoms to oxygen atoms in Al_2O_3 is 2 : 3, and here it is meaningful to add the '2' and '3' together to give '5', since this represents the *total number of atoms* in the formula. Thus, ⅖ of the atoms in aluminium oxide are oxygen atoms (or 0.4 or 40%).

5.7 Proportional reasoning and ratios

The following is an example of a calculation that appears to be relatively straightforward: $2\,cm^3$ of aluminium has a mass of 5.4 g. What is the mass of $4\,cm^3$? (Answer: 10.8 g)

The simplest method of arriving at the answer is to reason that doubling the volume (from $2\,cm^3$ to $4\,cm^3$) will double the mass (from $5.4\,g$ to $10.8\,g$). Although this seems intuitive, it does in fact involve a rather subtle idea – in effect, *comparing two ratios* to find x:

volume 1 (cm^3) : volume 2 (cm^3) = mass 1 (g) : mass 2 (g)

$$2:4 = 5.4:x$$

Finding the value of x from these ratios involves **proportional** reasoning. While using these simple ratios might not be too difficult, it becomes conceptually harder when the mental manipulation of the values is more challenging. For example, $17\,cm^3$ of aluminium has a mass of $91.8\,g$. What is the mass of $63\,cm^3$?

In such a case, it may be easier to do this as a two-stage calculation, working out first the density of aluminium (i.e. the mass of $1\,cm^3$). This value can then be used to calculate the mass of $63\,cm^3$ of aluminium.

For further details about different calculation strategies, see Chapter 9 *Scientific models and mathematical equations* on page 87.

5.8 Percentages

A **percentage** is a kind of fraction that relates a *part* to a *whole*. Using a percentage is helpful when comparing one thing to another, because it can avoid unwieldy fractions or decimals.

For example, if a population of 200 rabbits (the *whole*) has 60 males (the *part*) then the proportion of males in the population can be expressed in any of the following ways:

$$\frac{60}{200} \qquad \frac{3}{10} \qquad \frac{30}{100} \qquad 30\%$$

Thus, if the proportion of the part to the whole is expressed as a fraction with 100% as the denominator then the percentage is the numerator:

$$\frac{part}{whole} = \frac{percentage}{100\%}$$

This equation can be rearranged so that any one of these values (part, whole or percentage) can be calculated from values for the other two (for details of rearranging equations, see Chapter 9 *Scientific models and mathematical equations* on page 87). For example, a percentage can be calculated from:

$$percentage = \frac{part}{whole} \times 100\%$$

However, difficulties in calculations involving percentages can arise because of confusion over what the 'part' and the 'whole' represent. Avoiding the inappropriate use of formulae requires an understanding of what the percentage means in the context of the problem. For example, a percentage may apply to a part of an existing whole, or to an increase, or to a decrease.

The following questions are represented visually in Figure 5.7, which emphasises the meaning of the percentage in each case.

(a) A population of 200 rabbits has 30% males. How many males are there? (Answer: 60 male rabbits)

(b) A population of 200 rabbits increases by 30%. How big is the population after the change? (Answer: 260 rabbits)

(c) A population of 200 rabbits decreases by 30%. How big is the population after the change? (Answer: 140 rabbits)

Figure 5.7 Different meanings of a percentage

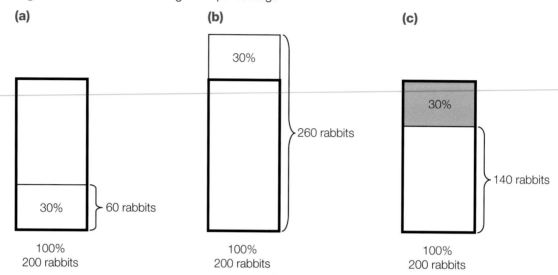

Pupils can get a better feeling for the idea that a percentage represents a fraction (a part of a whole) if they are familiar with some common examples: 50% represents ½, 25% represents ¼, 20% represents ⅕, and so on.

Note that, although percentages can be effective for communicating values, they may not always be the most useful form for doing calculations. For example, saying that something has a 10% chance of happening is the same as saying that it has a probability of 0.1; the former communicates a clear message but the latter is more convenient for use in calculations on probabilities.

5.9 Scale drawings and images

To **scale** a quantity means to enlarge or reduce it by a given amount. A **scale drawing** of an object is one in which all of the dimensions of the original object are multiplied by a constant. This constant is called the **scale factor** (another example of a **constant of proportionality**). Pupils encounter scale drawings in biology (e.g. images of microscopic organisms) and in physics (e.g. representations of forces).

If the scale factor is *greater than 1* then this produces an *enlarged* image (e.g. a drawing of a bacterium). If the value of the scale factor is *between 0 and 1* then this produces a *reduced* image (e.g. a map).

In the example shown in Figure 5.8, the original on the left has been *reduced* 3 times to produce the scale drawing on the right, i.e. the scale factor is ⅓. Every measurement is scaled by the same factor, so A_2 is ⅓ times A_1, and B_2 is ⅓ times B_1.

Figure 5.8 Original image and scale drawing

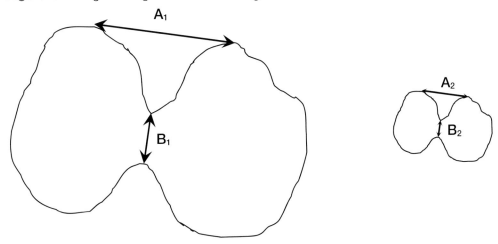

Another way of representing the scale factor would be to say that the scale of the drawing is 1:3. Note that, in this ratio, the first number represents the dimension of the scale drawing and the second number represents the dimension of the original. Other examples of scales as ratios would be a model aeroplane with a scale of 1:72 and a map with a scale of 1:50 000.

For drawings and photographs of microscopic objects, where the image is enlarged, the scale factor is usually represented as a magnification. For example, '100×' may appear next to an image meaning that it is 100 times larger than the original (i.e. the scale factor is 100). Interpreting such images requires an understanding both of scaling and of the units used to describe the sizes of microscopic objects (see Section 2.6 *Dealing with very large and very small values* on page 20).

Note that the scale factor applies only to the **_linear dimensions_**. For the effects of scaling on areas and volumes, see Chapter 10 *Mathematics and the real world* on page 107.

6　Dealing with variability

Key words: variability, random error, true value, uncertainty, population, sample, distribution, histogram, batch, class interval, frequency, average, mean, arithmetic mean, median, mode, spread, range, quartile, interquartile range, box plot, outlier, anomaly, probability, independent events, combined events, risk.

Variability in a set of data relates to how spread out or how close together the values are (the distribution of values). Although variability can arise for various reasons, the questions of interest, and the mathematical techniques used to answer them, are similar. These questions are:

- How big is a typical value?
- How much do the values vary?
- Are there any unusual values?

6.1　Where does variability come from?

A familiar example of *variability* is the way that people are different to each other. For example, some people run faster than others. In a 100 metres race, we would not expect all the runners to get exactly the same time – there would be a range of values. For a random sample of people, there would be lot of variability, i.e. a wide spread of values. For a race with elite runners, the times would be faster but also much closer to each other, and thus less variability.

A very different example is rolling a marble down a slope. If all the conditions were kept exactly the same, using identical marbles down identical slopes, then in principle we might expect to get exactly the same time for every run. However, in practice, it is likely that there will be some variability in the values. This variability does not result from differences between what is being measured, but in the act of measurement itself. Repeated measurements of the same thing may be different from each other because of measurement uncertainty.

The distinction between these is very important to understand. For all measurements there is *uncertainty in the measured values*, so this may always be a source of variability in repeated measurements. Variability can also arise from *differences between the individuals in a population*. Examples of these two sources of variability are:

- *Measurement uncertainty (for repeated measurements of the same thing)*
  - time of travel of a marble rolling down a slope
  - height of a bouncing ball dropped from a particular height
  - time for a paper parachute to fall
  - volume of a solution used in a titration.

- *Differences between individuals (for measurements of a sample of different but related things)*
  - time to run 100 metres for different people
  - height of pupils in a year group
  - number of spines on holly leaves
  - air pollution levels in different locations.

Understanding the differences between these two sources of variability is important, for example in appreciating the difference between line graphs and scatter graphs (see Section 3.6 *Line graphs and scatter graphs: two related quantities* on page 29). For '*line graph*' type data, the data points may not all lie on a fitted line because of *measurement uncertainty*; for '*scatter graph*' type data, a fitted line may not pass at all close to many of the data points because of differences between individuals.

6.2 Variability and measurement uncertainty

The reason for making repeated measurements in an experiment is because of **random error**. The experimental design should aim to minimise these errors but they cannot be eliminated. Thus any single measurement may be different from the **true value**, and repeated measurements may be different from each other. This **variability** is called the **uncertainty**. It depends both on the nature of the measuring instrument and on what is being measured.

For example, when using a ruler divided into millimetres, it is not difficult to measure the width of a sheet of paper to the nearest millimetre. Using a ruler divided into centimetres makes this harder. An estimate can be made by eye to the nearest millimetre, but with greater uncertainty than using the first ruler. The second ruler has a *lower resolution*, and the uncertainty is due to the nature of the measuring instrument.

By contrast, the uncertainty in measuring by eye the height to which a ball bounces is related more to the nature of what is being measured than to the measuring instrument. One can use a metre rule divided into millimetres but the movement of the ball means that it is really only possible to measure its position to the nearest centimetre.

A metre rule is an example of an *analogue* instrument, for which the resolution is related to the size of the scale divisions. On a *digital* instrument, the resolution is determined by the digits shown on the display.

For example, many digital thermometers read to the nearest 0.1 °C – this is its *resolution*. If the temperature of some warm water is measured as 32.6 °C then this suggests that the true value lies closer to this value than to 32.5 °C or 32.7 °C. However, if a second digital thermometer is used to measure the same temperature, it may display 32.9 °C. It is quite usual for different measuring instruments to give different measurements for the same thing. How close a reading is to the true value is related to the *accuracy* of the instrument. Thus the uncertainty in a measurement may be related to the instrument's accuracy and not its resolution.

The uncertainty in using a digital instrument, as for an analogue instrument, may also be related to the nature of what is being measured. If the temperature of the system being investigated changes very rapidly then it may only be possible to make measurements by eye to the nearest 1 °C even though the thermometer reads to the nearest 0.1 °C.

In 11–16 science, the uncertainty of a measurement relates to the number of significant figures in the value. For example, giving the mass of an object as 12 g suggests a greater uncertainty in its value than if it is given as 12.39 g. The number of significant figures is a reflection of the precision of the measurement. (See Section 1.2 *Measurement, resolution and significant figures* on page 9.)

In scientific practice, and in post-16 science, measurement uncertainty is indicated *explicitly* using the '±' symbol to show the range within which the true value is likely to lie. For example, the manufacturers of a digital thermometer may state that its accuracy is ±0.3 °C, so a measurement with this thermometer might be written as 32.6 °C ± 0.3 °C. This means that the true value is likely to be found in the range 32.3 °C to 32.9 °C. Note that it does not mean that the true value is *definitely* in this range but that there is a good *probability* that it is (often the probability value used is 95%).

It is important to note that the accuracy of the instrument (±0.3 °C) is not the same as its resolution (0.1 °C). They are, however, related through the choices made in the design of the instrument. It would be possible to make a digital thermometer with an accuracy of ±0.3 °C but with a digital display that could show values to the nearest 0.001 °C. There would be no point to this and it would be confusing. A display that reads to the nearest 0.1 °C is adequate for the accuracy of this particular thermometer.

In summary, measurement uncertainty depends on the resolution of the instrument, the accuracy of the instrument and on the nature of what is being measured. It is a complex and subtle area, where there are no simple rules about rounding and significant figures for measured and calculated values. Attempting to invent artificial rules for 11–16 science is neither desirable nor possible. To develop pupils' understanding, it is better if they think about the nature of each situation and make sensible judgements.

Finding the **mean** of a set of repeated measurements can reduce the uncertainty and give a value that is more likely to be closer to the true value than any single measurement.

In secondary school science experiments, a common rule of thumb is to take *three* repeated measurements (unless there is poor agreement between the results, suggesting that further measurement is needed). In scientific work, there is nothing 'special' about three repeated measurements. The choice of how many repeated measurements to take depends on their variability. School activities are usually designed so that random errors are relatively small. Taking more than three repeated measurements is time consuming, while with only two measurements there is a chance that the values may be in agreement but both incorrect. Three measurements is a reasonable compromise for most contexts in school science.

For example, the travel time of a marble rolling down a slope could be measured using a stopwatch. These times would be subject to random errors; for example, the watch might not be started and stopped at exactly the same point on each run.

If the measured times are 4.37 s, 4.72 s and 4.48 s then an answer to the question 'How big is a typical value?' can be found by calculating the mean. Dividing the sum of the values by the number of values using a typical calculator produces a value that may be displayed as 4.523333333. Rounding this value to three significant figures (the same as for the measured times) gives 4.52 s. The stopwatch reads to the nearest 0.01 s but the spread in the values suggests that the random errors in timing by hand are somewhat larger than this. In this case, it may make more sense to round to only two significant figures, i.e. 4.5 s. Thus, for these data, the value of 4.5 s is our best guess of the *true value* of the travel time. (For more about means and significant figures, see Section 2.4 *Calculating means* on page 18.)

For further information about the measurement uncertainty, see the ASE/Nuffield publication *The Language of Measurement.*

6.3 Variability in a population of individuals

Many biological experiments involve making measurements on a *sample* of individuals in a *population*. Here, the *variability* is not due to random error but because of differences between the individuals in the sample. The variability relates to what is of interest about the sample itself and not about the way the values are measured. (For further details about sampling, see Section 8.2 *Populations and samples* on page 76.)

For example, suppose a group of four girls aged 15 run a 100 metres race. Their times are measured as 14.5 s, 13.9 s, 15.3 s and 14.8 s. Although there will be random errors in these measurements, the variability here is caused mainly by *differences in the individuals themselves*. Some girls can run faster than others.

An answer to the question 'How big is a typical value?' can again be found by calculating the mean – for these data it is 14.6 s. If the girls are reasonably representative of their age group then this value is our best guess of the typical running time for 100 metres of a 15-year-old girl. Of course, this is a small sample and the girls might not be at all representative of the population. So, our guess might not in fact be a *good* guess for the typical running time but, in the absence of any other data, this is our *best* guess.

Not all populations of individuals are biological. In manufacturing, the objects being made can be thought of as populations. For example, in making pistons for a particular car engine, the sizes of each should in principle be identical. In practice, there will be some variability in this 'population', but the aim of the production process is to keep this variability within acceptable limits.

With only three or four individuals, taking a mean is about as much as can be done. However, experiments and surveys that look at samples of populations often collect data on relatively large numbers of individuals. With larger samples, there is more that can be explored, and it is useful to have techniques for seeing patterns in large data sets.

6.4 Displaying larger sets of values

A useful way of displaying the *distribution* of a larger number of values is to draw a *histogram*. For example, the first column in Figure 6.1 shows a set of measurements of the heights of a sample of 12- to 13-year-old pupils (in cm). A data set such as this, which contains a set of values related to a single quantity, is sometimes referred to as a *batch* of data. Just looking at the raw data gives a sense of how big the values are, but organising the data enables more to be seen.

The next step here is to order the raw data in order of size. Figure 6.1b shows a column of values going from the highest down to the lowest. (A quick method for ordering sets of values is described in Section 8.3 *Analysing a batch of data* on page 77.) It is now easier to get a sense by eye of the variation in these values.

Figure 6.1 Heights of pupils in a sample (cm)

(a) Raw   **(b)** Ordered   **(c)** Put into classes   **(d)** Histogram

(a) Raw	(b) Ordered	(c) Put into classes	
153	168	168	
155	164	164	Frequency = 4
163	163	163	
153	163	163	
164	158	158	
143	155	155	
158	153	153	Frequency = 5
148	153	153	
142	151	151	
168	149	149	
144	149	149	
149	148	148	
163	147	147	Frequency = 8
137	144	144	
149	143	143	
141	142	142	
151	141	141	
147	137	137	Frequency = 1

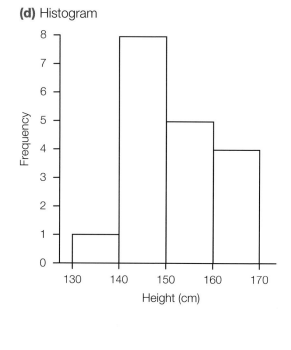

In order to draw a histogram, the next step is to split the set of values into a number of groups or 'classes' – the **class interval** is the range of values within each class. The choice of class interval should result in a sensible number of classes, neither too few nor too many. A convenient choice is 130–139 cm, 140–149 cm, 150–159 cm and 160–169 cm.

The data values in each class are counted to give the total number or **frequency** for each class as shown in Figure 6.1c. For example, there are four data values in the class interval 160–169 cm (163, 163, 164 and 168), so it has a frequency of 4.

Note that discrete data can also be put into groups like this (for an example, see Section 3.2 *Using tables to process data* on page 24, which discusses the construction of a frequency table from discrete data).

Figure 6.1d shows a histogram drawn from these values. The height of each bar shows the frequency of values (i.e. the number of values) within each class interval (i.e. the range of values of the bar).

This set of data has a fairly small number of values. With a larger number of values, a smaller class interval could be chosen (say 5 cm instead of 10 cm), so that each bar represents a narrower range of values. The histogram would then have more bars and give a better indication of the distribution of values. With only a small number of values, this would not be a good idea since there would not be many values in each of the classes. Choosing an appropriate width for the class interval is entirely a matter of judgement.

It is important not to confuse a histogram with a **bar chart**, since they are very different. A histogram shows the frequency distribution of a set of values, and the horizontal axis represents a **quantitative** (**continuous** or **discrete**) variable. To indicate this, the columns are drawn touching each other. By contrast, in a bar chart the horizontal axis represents a **qualitative** (**categorical**) variable and the columns are drawn with spaces in between (see Section 3.4 *Charts showing a quantity categorised by one factor* on page 26 for further details).

Note that there are differences between mathematics and science in the meaning of 'histogram'. For the histogram in Figure 6.1, the width of each column (the class interval) has been chosen to be the same. This is the usual practice in scientific literature and in school science.

In mathematics, pupils learn to draw histograms in which the class intervals (and hence the width of the columns) are different from each other; the vertical axis represents 'frequency density' and not frequency. Frequency density is calculated by dividing the frequency of the class interval by the width of the class interval, and so the frequency for each class is represented by the area of the column and not by its height.

If all the columns are the same width then the shape of the display is the same regardless of whether frequency density or frequency is plotted.

In science, a 'histogram' is generally taken to mean a plot of *frequency*, with all the class intervals being the *same width*. Since this is what pupils will encounter in science textbooks, it is this meaning that is used in this publication. Teachers and pupils need to be aware of this difference in the meaning of histogram in mathematics and science.

6.5   How big is a typical value?

Just by looking at the values for the example above, it is easy to see that a typical value is somewhere between 140 cm and 160 cm. Mathematically, three measures may be used to express this idea of a 'typical value' or 'central tendency' – *mean*, *median* and *mode*:

- **Mean** (strictly speaking the **arithmetic mean**): For this set of values, the sum of the heights is 2728 cm and the number of values is 18, so the mean is 151.6 cm. One problem with a mean is that it can be affected by **outliers** (unusually high or low values), since it uses *all* values as part of the calculation.

- **Median**: This is the middle value of a distribution, and can easily be found once the values have been ordered. If there is an even number of values (as here), the median is the mean of the middle two: these are 149 cm and 151 cm, so the median is 150 cm.

- **Mode**: In a distribution of **discrete** values, the mode is the most common value. Some sets of data may have more than one mode. For the data shown in Figure 6.1 (**continuous** data, not discrete), the interval with the largest number of values (in this case 140–149 cm) is the *modal interval*.

The mean, the median and the mode are all ways of expressing an **average**. In everyday language, the word 'average' is generally used as an alternative term for 'arithmetic mean'. In science and mathematics, this usage should be avoided, since an 'average' refers to any measure of a typical value of a distribution.

In summary, three ways of expressing an average for these data are:

- mean = 151.6 cm
- median = 150 cm
- modal interval = 140–149 cm.

The mean is the most familiar and the one most commonly used in school science. An advantage of a median is that, unlike a mean, its value is not affected by *outliers*; a median can also be quicker to find than a mean.

When talking about an average as being a 'typical value', it is important to emphasise that it does not mean 'the most common value'. For example, saying that a typical value for these data is 150 cm does *not* mean that most of these pupils are 150 cm tall. Instead, think of it as just meaning 'roughly how big'. For an alien who did not know whether a 12- to 13-year-old was nearer 10 nanometres or 10 metres tall, saying that a 'typical value' is 150 cm gives a good sense of size.

6.6 How much do the values vary?

In addition to having a way of indicating a 'typical value' for a set of data, it is useful to have a measure of how spread out the values are. Two commonly used measures of **spread** are the **range** and the **interquartile range**.

The **range** is the *difference* between the highest and lowest values. For these data, the range is 31 cm (168 cm − 137 cm). Note that in school science, the 'range' of a set of data is generally used to indicate the lowest and highest values (e.g. the range is 'from 137 cm to 168 cm'). Since this meaning differs from the one used in mathematics and statistics, pupils should be told explicitly what they should do if they are asked to find the range of a set of data (e.g. 'write down the highest and lowest values' or 'calculate the difference between the highest and lowest values'). Although it is easy to calculate, a problem in using the range is that it is affected by extreme values at the high end or low end of the distribution (outliers).

Figure 6.2 shows another way of representing a distribution visually. It is called a **box plot**, and these types of display are very effective at showing the variation in values. To construct a box plot, the first step is to identify the highest and lowest values, and the median. This is shown in Figure 6.2a.

Figure 6.2 A box plot is another way of displaying a distribution of values

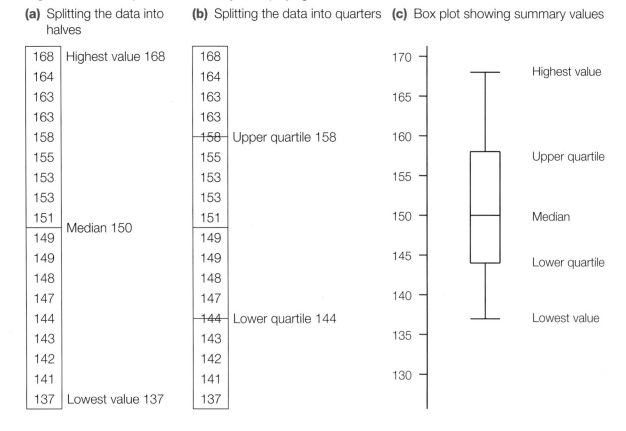

(a) Splitting the data into halves   **(b)** Splitting the data into quarters   **(c)** Box plot showing summary values

Finding the median can be thought of as splitting the data set into two halves – the median is the value where the data set is split. The next step is to split each of these two halves again in halves. Thus, the data set has now been split into four quarters, and this is represented in Figure 6.2b. The values where the upper and lower halves of the data are split are called the **quartiles**.

The *upper quartile* is the middle of the top half of the data (in this case, the middle of the largest nine values is 158 cm) and the *lower quartile* is the middle of the bottom half of the data (in this case, 144 cm). These five 'summary' values (highest value, upper quartile, median, lower quartile and lowest value) can now be used to draw the box plot shown in Figure 6.2c. (See Section 8.3 *Analysing a batch of data* on page 77 for further details of how to draw a box plot.)

The central box of a box plot is a better indication of the *spread* of values than the *range*, since it is not distorted by outliers. It represents the **interquartile range**, which is the difference between the upper quartile and the lower quartile. Here, its value is 14 cm (158 cm − 144 cm).

The line extending above the box represents the upper quarter of the values and the line below represents the lower quarter of the values. Thus, the central box represents *one half of the values in the distribution*: it indicates that the heights of half of the pupils in this sample lie between 144 cm and 158 cm.

Measures of spread are especially useful when comparing two or more data sets, and this is discussed in Section 8.5 *Comparing batches of data* on page 81.

6.7 Comparing shapes of distributions

Box plots and **histograms** are both helpful ways of displaying batches of data. The particular strength of the box plot is that when a number of them are drawn side-by-side, the eye can quickly scan across and compare the medians and spreads of different **distributions**. A histogram shows more detail about a distribution than the five summary values of a box plot but histograms are not as easy to interpret as box plots when comparing two or more batches of data.

Some distributions may be fairly symmetrical while others may be *skewed* – with values spread out on one side of the middle more than the other. The histogram in Figure 6.3a represents a fairly symmetrical distribution. This kind of distribution is what one might expect when measuring the heights of a sample of pupils of the same age. By contrast, the histogram in Figure 6.3b represents a skewed distribution, with values clustered more at the upper end.

This kind of distribution, with values skewed towards the right, is typical when there is some kind of 'ceiling'. A distribution of the heights of a random sample of people from babies to adults would have a 'ceiling' effect: adults tend not to go over a certain height, while the heights of babies and children would be spread out over lower values.

The box plots for these two distributions are shown in Figure 6.3c. The shape of the box plot on the left indicates that it is a roughly symmetrical distribution, since the median is approximately in the middle of the box and the lengths of the lines above and below the box are about equal. The box plot on the right clearly shows a skewed distribution, with the lower part being 'stretched out' and the upper part being 'squashed together'.

Figure 6.3 Comparing distributions

(a) Histogram representing a fairly symmetrical distribution

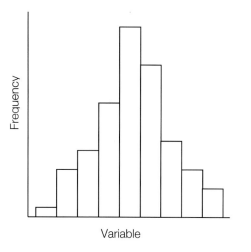

(b) Histogram representing a skewed distribution

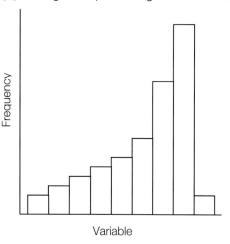

(c) Using box plots to compare the two distributions

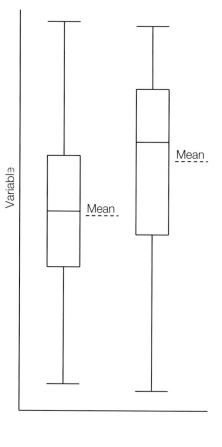

It may seem intuitively obvious that, in any distribution, roughly half of the values will be below average, and half above average. However, this is not always the case. If the *median* is taken as the average then it will be true: the median splits the set of data into two, so there are equal numbers of values above and below the median. However, if the *arithmetic mean* is taken as the average then the number of values above and below the mean will depend on the shape of the distribution.

This is illustrated by the box plots in Figure 6.3c. For the first box plot, the distribution is fairly symmetrical and the mean is approximately the same as the median: the numbers of values above and below the mean are about the same. However, for the second box plot, the distribution is *positively skewed* and the value of the mean lies *below* the median: for this distribution there are more values above the mean than below it.

6.8 Are there any unusual values?

An **outlier** is a value in a set of data that seems to be unusually large or unusually small in comparison with most of the other values. For repeated measurements, an outlier may be the result of a mistake and is often disregarded. For measurements on a sample of individuals, an outlier may indicate a value that is of particular interest. There are no hard-and-fast rules for how to identify and deal with outliers – it will depend on the context.

Note that 'outlier' is a statistical term that can be used to describe unusual values in *any* kind of distribution. The term *anomaly* (or 'anomalous value') is also used in school science, though usually in the context of repeated measurements rather than for individuals in a population. For example, a bowhead whale has a particularly long lifespan for a mammal but it is not generally regarded as being an 'anomaly' (see Section 8.3 *Analysing a batch of data* on page 77).

The heights of pupils in the sample shown in Figure 6.1 ranged from 137 cm to 168 cm. Suppose another value was added to this – a very low one of 48 cm. The value stands out as very different from the rest. One possibility is that it is a mistake – perhaps the actual value was 148 cm and it was written down incorrectly. If a value is a mistake then it should be corrected or removed. Another possibility is that the value is indeed correct but unusual. In this particular example, it is unlikely that there would be a pupil of this height but, in other situations, it is quite possible that there may be an unusual value that genuinely represents a special case. Identifying and displaying such outliers can be useful as there can be interesting and important reasons why they are very different from the rest of the values. (See Section 8.3 *Analysing a batch of data* on page 77 for further details.)

6.9   Basic ideas in probability

A deeper understanding of variability can be gained by using ideas about probability, since randomness is an underlying cause of the variation. Probability is an important topic of study in 11–16 mathematics, though in science at this level it appears very little, except for some basic ideas related to genetics. However, in science itself, probabilistic ideas have a very significant place – both in understanding a wide variety of phenomena and in the design of experiments and handling measurement uncertainty. Pupils will meet these ideas much more in post-16 science.

A simple example of something that produces random outcomes is tossing a coin. The outcome cannot be predicted but there is an equal chance of getting a head or a tail. This is described as saying that the *probability* of getting the head is ½, 0.5 or 50%. The probability of getting a tail is the same. The sum of these two probabilities (½ + ½) is equal to 1. A probability of 1 means that something is *certain* to happen, i.e. the coin will either land as a head or as a tail (ignoring the very unlikely outcome that it lands exactly on its edge).

If a coin is tossed and a head is obtained then the probabilities of getting a head or a tail on the second toss are still the same. The outcome of the second throw is not affected by the outcome of the first throw. Each coin toss is therefore called an *independent event*. (A dependent event is one whose probability is affected by the outcome of another event.) Many people do not find this idea at all intuitive and believe that if a coin is tossed five times and it lands as heads every time then the probability of getting a tail the next time will be much higher. However, since these are independent events, the probability of a head is still ½ (assuming it is a 'fair' coin).

If you toss a coin a very large number of times (say a billion times) then you would expect the proportions of heads and tails to be very close to 50% of each. However, if you only toss a coin 10 times (a small sample size), you might get 5 of each, but it is also quite likely you will get a different proportion, such as 4 heads and 6 tails. The larger the sample of tosses, the more likely you are to get closer to half being heads and half being tails.

If a coin is tossed twice, there are a total of *four* possible outcomes: HH, HT, TH and TT. These are shown in Figure 6.4 (this is known as a *sample space*).

Figure 6.4 Outcomes of tossing a coin twice

		2nd toss	
		H	T
1st toss	H	HH	HT
	T	TH	TT

A pair of coin tosses, consisting of two separate events, is an example of a **combined event**. The probability of a combined event can be calculated by multiplying together each of the probabilities of the separate events but *only* if these are *independent events*. So, for a pair of coin tosses, the probability of getting a head on the first toss is ½ and the probability of getting a head on the second toss is also ½. The probability of throwing two heads is therefore ½ × ½ = ¼. The probabilities for each of the four outcomes are shown in Figure 6.5a. All of them are ¼. This means that in a very large number of coin tosses, you would expect there to be 25% of each of the four combinations, as shown in Figure 6.5b.

Figure 6.5 Probabilities and percentage frequencies

(a) Probabilities for each combination

	H	T
H	¼	¼
T	¼	¼

(b) Outcome for very many pairs of coin tosses

	H	T
H	25%	25%
T	25%	25%

(c) A possible outcome for 100 pairs of coins tosses

	H	T
H	30%	19%
T	27%	24%

For a smaller number of pairs of coin tosses, you would not expect to get 25% of each combination. Figure 6.5c shows a possible outcome for 100 pairs of coin tosses. As the number of pairs of tosses increases, the more likely it is that the proportions will approach 25% of each.

These ideas about the outcomes of coin tossing are a direct analogy for the way that the outcomes of genetic crosses are predicted (and as represented using a Punnett square). The outcome of a single coin toss corresponds to a particular allele, while the pair of coin tosses corresponds to the pair of alleles inherited from each parent.

So far, we have looked at the outcomes of a single coin toss and of a pair of coin tosses. This can be continued, looking at the probabilities of each of the outcomes for three, four or more sets of coin tosses. The mathematical calculations get rather more difficult but the principle is just the same. Figure 6.6 shows the probabilities of possible outcomes for various numbers of coin tosses, expressed in terms of 'number of heads'.

For example, Figure 6.6a shows that, for a single coin toss, there are two outcomes: 0 heads (i.e. a tail) or 1 head. The probability of each is 0.5.

Figure 6.6b shows that, for two coin tosses, there are three outcomes: 0 heads (i.e. TT), 1 head (i.e. HT, TH) and 2 heads (HH). These probabilities are 0.25, 0.5 and 0.25, respectively.

Figure 6.6c shows the outcomes for three coin tosses and Figure 6.6d shows the outcomes for four coin tosses. For sets of four coin tosses, the most likely outcome is to get 2 heads (and thus 2 tails). Much less likely, though still quite possible, is to get 0 heads or 4 heads.

Figure 6.6 Probabilities of outcomes from various numbers of coin tosses

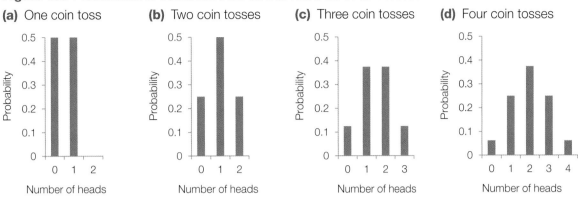

(a) One coin toss **(b)** Two coin tosses **(c)** Three coin tosses **(d)** Four coin tosses

We can carry on looking at larger and larger numbers of coin tosses. Figure 6.7 shows the probabilities of all the outcomes for sets of 10 coin tosses. It shows that 5 heads (and thus 5 tails) is the most likely but several other combinations can occur quite often; for example, getting 3 heads has a probability of over 0.1. The probability of getting 9 or 10 heads in 10 throws, however, is very low.

Figure 6.7 Probabilities of outcomes from 10 coin tosses

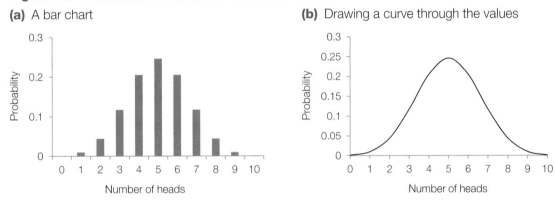

(a) A bar chart **(b)** Drawing a curve through the values

With this larger number of values, it is interesting to see the shape of the graph obtained by drawing a curve through these data points (Figure 6.7b). This shows the classic 'bell-shaped' curve – the sort of distribution that you get, for example, by measuring the heights of people in a population. Most people are of middling height with smaller numbers of very short or very tall people.

The shapes are similar for the same underlying reason. The heights of people, like the outcomes of coin tossing, are determined by a combination of many random events. The same is true for the variability due to measurement uncertainty (e.g. repeated measurements of the time for a marble to run down a slope) and for the natural variability in the characteristics of any population (e.g. the times for different people to run a 100 m race).

6.10 Estimating risks

In everyday language, the words 'hazard' and 'risk' are used more or less interchangeably with the word 'danger'. However, they are also technical terms with precise meanings. A *hazard* is something that is potentially harmful to people, property or the environment. A **risk** relates to the *probability* of harm occurring when exposed to a hazard. For example, a river near a house is a *hazard* because it can potentially cause flooding. The risk of the land around the house being flooded by the river might be assessed as a 1% annual probability.

There are essentially two ways in which risks can be assessed. Thinking about coin tosses is a simple way to illustrate this. If we want to know what the 'risk' is of getting two heads when we toss two coins, there are two ways of working this out.

One method is to collect a lot of data, by noting the outcomes of many pairs of coin tosses. The more coin tosses we do, the more likely the estimate is to be accurate. With a very large number of pairs of coin tosses, the 'risk' of getting two heads is found to be ¼.

The other method is to work out the probability from what we know about the behaviour of the coins. For each coin toss, the probability of getting a head is ½. Thus the 'risk' of getting two heads is ½ × ½ = ¼.

In the real word, both of these methods are used to calculate risks. When a lot of data is available, the first method can be used. The risk of getting lung cancer from smoking, or the risk of certain injuries in road accidents, can be found by analysing statistics that are routinely collected.

Other risks relate to events that happen rarely or have never happened. Calculating the risks of damage to a nuclear power station due to an earthquake, or the risks to human health on a mission to Mars, cannot be calculated by analysing large data sets of previous cases. Instead, they are calculated by combining the estimated probabilities of the events that lead to the outcomes being assessed.

Estimating risks in the real world is of course much harder than working out probabilities in coin tossing. For example, despite having a great deal of data about people's health and behaviour, it took a long time and much analysis before the link between smoking and lung cancer was established. In the case of nuclear power stations, different people may make different estimates of risk because they make different assumptions about the contributions to the risk.

6.11 Interpreting reports about risk

Everything that we do entails **risk**. Running, walking or any kind of physical activity involve the risk of injury, while lack of exercise is a risk to health. In order to make decisions, one needs to weigh up the sizes of different risks. There are frequent media reports concerning risk, such as the impact of new drugs or the effects of diet on health. However, people may have difficulties in understanding the figures, and the studies are often reported in a way that makes them hard to interpret. This can have a serious effect on the ways that risks are perceived.

For example, here are some headlines about cancer risks:
* 'CT scans in childhood can triple the chance of developing brain cancer'
* 'One drink a day increases breast cancer risk by 5%'.

The figures themselves may not be easy for many people to compare because they are expressed in different ways. A 'tripling' of a risk can re-expressed as a '200% increase' (conceptually not a simple calculation) and, put this way, perhaps it sounds more alarming (after all, '200' is a bigger number than '3'). When both figures are expressed as percentages, they can be compared more easily:
* 'CT scans in childhood can increase the risk of developing brain cancer by 200%'
* 'One drink a day increases breast cancer risk by 5%'.

A casual reading of these figures might suggest that childhood CT scans are a much bigger cancer risk than having one drink a day (40 times bigger).

However, the problem is that the figures in these headlines are referring to *relative risk* and not *absolute risk*. Your risk of being hit by a meteorite is extremely small indeed (an *absolute risk*); if for some reason this risk increases 100 times (a *relative risk*), this would still represent a very small risk of being hit. So, it is hard to interpret a relative risk without knowing the size of the underlying absolute risk.

For the two examples above, the relevant absolute risks are:
* about 1 in 10 000 children aged 0–9 develop brain tumours or leukaemia
* about 11% of women who do not drink develop breast cancers.

Again, some care is needed in comparing these figures for the absolute risk. Some people think that '1 in 10 000' is a bigger risk than '1 in 100' (since 10 000 is a big number), or that '1 in 10' is smaller than '5%'. Re-expressing the second risk allows the two risks to be compared more easily:
* about 1 in 10 000 children aged 0–9 develop brain tumours or leukaemia
* about 1100 in 10 000 women who do not drink develop breast cancers.

The story presented here has been simplified, but the principle should be clear to see. The *absolute risk* in the second example is far, far bigger than the first, even though the *relative risk* is lower. Using all the available data and some intricate calculations, studies have worked out the increase in numbers of cases:
* an extra two cases of cancer for every 10 000 children given CT scans
* an extra 60 cases of breast cancer for every 10 000 women who regularly have a drink.

The 'tripling' of cancer due to CT scans now seems to be less alarming than the headline may have suggested to many people. Although the relative risk is very high, the numbers affected are fairly small because of the low underlying absolute risk.

7 Looking for relationships: line graphs

> **Key words:** line graph, variable, linear, linear relationship, non-linear, gradient, origin, intercept, proportional, rate, line of best fit, interpolation, extrapolation, outlier.

Many investigations in science are concerned with finding relationships between continuous variables. After collecting a set of data, the data points for two variables can be plotted on a graph, and then a line drawn that best expresses the apparent relationship suggested by the data. This is called a line of best fit.

7.1 Types of relationship and shapes of line graphs

Before looking at drawing lines of best fit, it is useful to consider the possible kinds of relationship between variables that might be found. Figure 7.1 shows a number of different shapes of graphs – this selection is not intended to be comprehensive, but sufficient to illustrate a variety of relationships.

To avoid confusion among pupils, it is important to be aware that the term 'line' has a more precise meaning in mathematics than the way it is often used in science. In mathematics, a *line* (and thus a *line of best fit*) is, by definition, *straight*. In science, however, it is quite common to talk about 'straight lines' and 'curved lines' (which in mathematics would be called 'lines' and 'curves'). Changing habitual ways of talking is hard. A good compromise in science might be to refer to 'straight lines' and 'curves', though it may be hard to avoid using the term 'curved line of best fit'. Even though most of the graphs in Figure 7.1 show curves rather than straight lines, they are still all referred to as **line graphs**.

Some relationships in science can be described by relatively simple mathematical equations, while others are more complex. This section focuses just on the shapes of the line graphs and on fitting straight lines and curves to data points by eye; the use of mathematical equations is discussed later (see Chapter 9 *Scientific models and mathematical equations* on page 87).

Figure 7.1 A compendium of line graphs

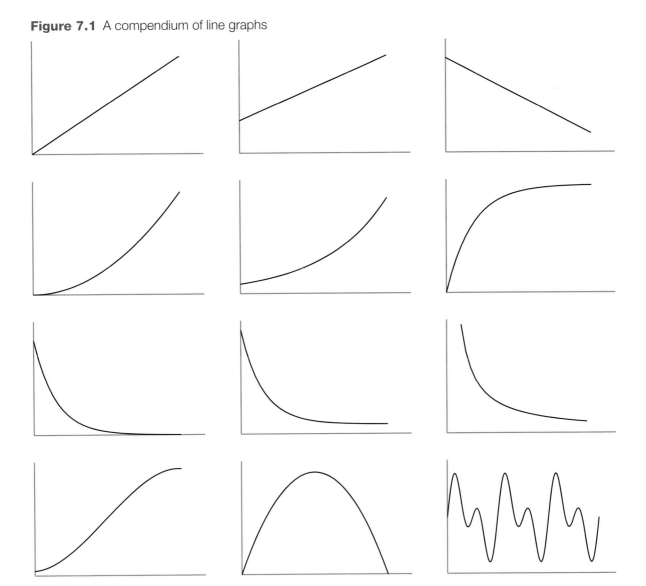

7.2 Developing a descriptive language

It is helpful for pupils to develop ways of identifying and describing the nature of the relationships shown in **line graphs**. This does not mean simply describing the *superficial shape* of the line, which they might find quite easy to do. What is harder for them is to relate the shape to the *meaning* of the relationship between the real-world **variables**. This needs building up with practice, using graphs they draw from their own results, as well as completed graphs presented to them. The following discussion includes suggested phrases that can be used as part of such descriptions.

When interpreting a graph, the first thing always is to pay attention to *what the graph is about*, i.e. the variables involved, as indicated by the labels on the axes, and any other information. It is also essential to be aware of the *range for each axis*, since this affects the visual appearance of the graph (see Section 4.3 *Choosing the range of each axis* on page 37). This is particularly important when comparing two or more similar graphs.

Note that since the graphs shown below are intended to be 'abstract' they do not have the axes labelled with particular variables. The discussion will therefore be in terms of changes to '*x*' and '*y*'. In a real context, the names of the variables would be used to give the descriptions a real-world meaning.

When thinking about the meaning of the line on a graph, a starting point is to identify whether the line goes up or down. For the graphs in Figure 7.2a, '*as x increases, y increases*'; for those in Figure 7.2b, '*as x increases, y decreases*'. This distinction is a very basic aspect of a relationship, and indeed does not really need a graph to be able to identify – it would be obvious from the table of results. Note that some graphs do not simply go either up or down, and these will be discussed later.

Figure 7.2 Increasing and decreasing

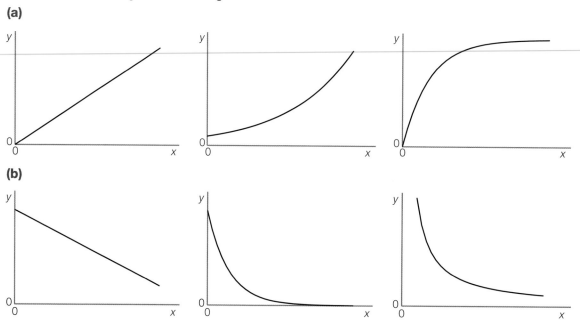

What we can see from a line graph, but would not be so obvious from the table of results, is whether the line is straight or curved. So, we could talk of a '*straight line graph*' for which '*as x increases, y steadily increases*' (Figure 7.3a) or for which '*as x increases, y steadily decreases*' (Figure 7.3b). The term 'steadily' is a rather informal term but it gives a good sense of what is happening.

Figure 7.3 Graphs with straight lines

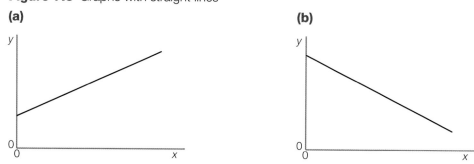

The relationships shown in '*curved graphs*' are more complex to describe. One possibility is that '*as x increases, y increases slowly at first and then more rapidly*' (Figure 7.4a) or that '*as x increases, y increases rapidly at first and then more slowly*' (Figure 7.4b). Similar descriptions can be used for the curved graphs that show a '*decrease of y with x*'.

The formal term to describe a straight line graph is **linear**, whether or not it goes through the origin, and the relationship between the two variables is called a **linear relationship**. Similarly, the relationship shown by a curved graph is called **non-linear**.

Figure 7.4 Graphs with curves

(a)

(b)

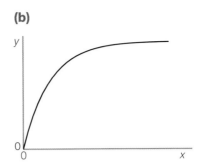

When we talk of a variable changing 'slowly' or 'rapidly', we are using these terms in a relative sense to describe how the **gradient** (or *slope*) of a line changes. For a linear relationship, the gradient at any point along the line is the same. For a curve, the gradient varies at different points along the curve.

An important feature of a relationship is whether the line goes through the **origin** (the point at which the values of *x* and *y* are zero). Figures 7.5a and 7.5b are both linear relationships. However, while the first shows '*a straight line that goes through the origin*', the second shows '*a straight line with an intercept on the y-axis*'. The point at which it meets the *y*-axis is called the **intercept**. Figure 7.5a shows a **proportional** relationship, i.e. doubling the value of *x* doubles the value of *y*. So '*as x increases, y increases, and y is proportional to x*'. However, although Figure 7.5b represents a *linear* relationship, it is not a *proportional* relationship, since the line does not go through the origin. (See Section 9.11 *Mathematical equations and relationships in science* on page 99.)

Figure 7.5 Straight line graphs and the origin

(a)

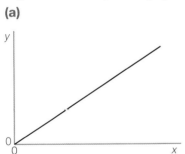

(b)

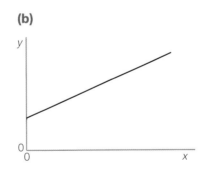

Finally, while some curves may appear to increase indefinitely (Figure 7.6a), others may '*level out towards a maximum*' (Figure 7.6b). Similarly, other curves showing decreasing values may '*level out towards a minimum*' (Figure 7.6c).

Figure 7.6 Some curves tend towards a maximum or a minim level

(a)

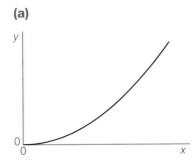

(b)

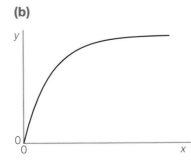

(c)

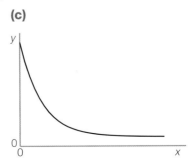

The graph shown in Figure 7.7 provides an opportunity to put all of these ideas together. Relevant phrases might be: *'curved graph'*, *'intercept on y-axis'*, *'as x increases, y increases'*, *'y increases slowly at first, then more rapidly, then slows down again'* and *'reaches a maximum level'*.

Figure 7.7 A more complex shape

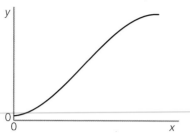

So far, all of the graphs discussed have had a line that either always goes up or always goes down (the technical term for this is *monotonic*). Other relationships are more complex, with lines than can go up and down (called *non-monotonic*).

The last two examples are included to illustrate this. Figure 7.8a could represent the height of a ball as it is thrown in the air and then falls to the ground. Figure 7.8b could represent the amplitude of a loudspeaker producing a musical note. Since the pattern repeats, it can be called periodic (another example would be a sine wave).

Figure 7.8 Some curves are neither 'up' nor 'down'

(a)

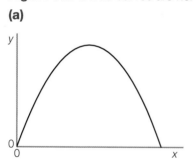

(b)

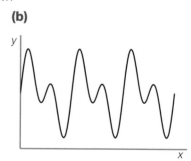

7.3 Gradients and rates of change

Many graphs have 'time' as the variable on the horizontal axis, and indeed the language that we use reflects this. For example, Figure 7.9a shows a graph that represents the progress of a chemical reaction between a carbonate and an acid to produce carbon dioxide. At first, the increase in the volume of carbon dioxide is quite fast but then it slows down. Notice how a graph reflects the way we use language to describe how the sizes of things can go *up and down* (represented on the *vertical* axis) and happen *one thing after another* in time (represented from left to right on the *horizontal* axis).

On a graph that shows a change over time, the steepness of the line represents how fast the change is happening. In other words, the **gradient** of the line represents a **rate** of change. Since, this is the rate of change at a *particular instant in time*, it is called an *instantaneous* rate of change.

Figure 7.9b shows the way that the current through a filament bulb varies with the potential difference across it. The curve has a shape that has some similarities to the previous graph (note that it is not linear and does not follow Ohm's Law). Even though it does not represent a change over time, we may still use the same language to describe it – rising rapidly at first and then more slowly. It is also possible to use the term 'rate' to describe the gradient here as well, i.e. as 'the rate at which current changes with potential difference'). When talking about relationships between variables in 11–16 science, however, *rate* is usually only used to refer to a *rate of change over time*.

Figure 7.9 Some changes are against time, others are not

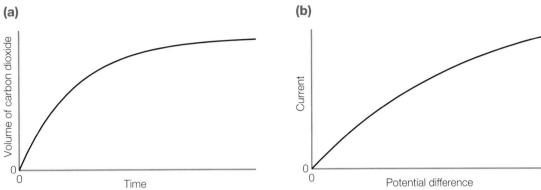

(a)

(b)

7.4   Lines of best fit: linear relationships

Sometimes it happens that when the data points from an experiment are plotted, a straight line can be drawn which appears to pass *exactly* through all of the points. More usually, even if the underlying relationship is linear, the data points do not lie exactly on a straight line because of measurement uncertainty. In such a case, a **line of best fit** may be found that passes as close as possible to the points.

It is important to be clear about the meaning of a fitted line *for data of this kind*. It has a very different meaning to the line segments on a graph where each pair of data points are joined; it also has a very different meaning from a line of best fit on a scatter graph (see Section 3.6 *Line graphs and scatter graphs: two related quantities* on page 29).

These differences arise because of the differences in the nature of the data. For 'line graph' type data, the data points may not all lie on the fitted line because of *measurement uncertainty*. For 'scatter graph' type data, the differences from a fitted line are due to *differences between individuals in a population*. The distinction between these two different kinds of variability is discussed in Section 6.1 *Where does variability come from?* on page 50.

Figure 7.10a shows a set of eight data points plotted on a graph (for convenience, the discussions in this chapter on drawing lines of best fit use 'abstract' graphs with no variables specified). Inspecting these points by eye suggests that this may be a **linear relationship**, so a straight line could be fitted. A useful technique with points plotted on graph paper is to hold the paper almost at right angles to your face and then to rotate the paper to look down along the direction of the data points. This is a quick way of seeing how close the points would be to a straight line.

To draw a line on graph paper, it is better to have a *transparent* ruler so that all of the data points can be seen. Figure 7.10b shows a line of fit drawn by eye. It seems to be quite a good fit as it passes close to all of the points. But what is meant by a line of *best* fit?

Figure 7.10 A good line of fit

(a)   **(b)**

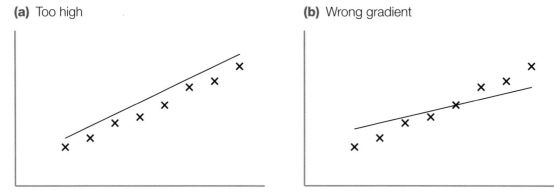

Figure 7.11 shows two lines that are most definitely not good lines of fit. The 'badness' of fit has been deliberately exaggerated in each case to illustrate the criteria for fitting a good line. In Figure 7.11a, the gradient of the line matches the gradient of the data points but the line is too high. In the good line of fit, there were data points on *both sides* of the line, but here they are all *below* the line. By contrast, in Figure 7.11b, there are similar numbers of points above and below the line but the gradient of the line is wrong. All the points below the line are on the left and all the points above the line are on the right.

Figure 7.11 What makes a bad line of fit?

(a) Too high   **(b)** Wrong gradient

So, when drawing a line by hand on graph paper, there are two things to think about: getting the height of the ruler right and getting its slope right, so that the line is as close to all the points as possible. Sometimes a line may pass though some of the points but this is not essential – it is possible to have a line of best fit that does not actually pass through any of the points.

There are no hard-and-fast rules for producing a 'best fit' by eye; it is a matter of judgement to find the one that looks best. When a line of best fit is done by a computer, various rules are used to decide exactly what is meant by 'as close to all the points as possible'. However, even with a computer, there is no single method to produce a 'unique' best line, and different rules may produce different 'best' lines.

7.5   Interpolation and extrapolation on a line graph

The graph in Figure 7.10a had eight data points, each representing a value for *y* corresponding to a particular value of *x*. Once a line of best fit has been drawn, it is possible to use it to estimate a value for *y* corresponding to *any* value for *x*. Figure 7.12a illustrates how a value for *y* can be 'read off' the graph for a value of *x* that is in between the original data points. This technique is called ***interpolation***. It can be used, for example, in calibrating instruments such as thermometers – a number of measurements are made to create a calibration curve (or straight line), and this is used to infer all of the other values.

Getting good estimates from interpolation assumes that the fitted line is a good representation of what happens in between the measured data points, and that there are no unexpected variations. The more measurements that are made, the greater the chance that interpolation will give good estimates. In fact, since the fitted line may compensate for measurement uncertainties in the data, it can actually give better estimates of the y values for the original data points than the actual data values themselves. This is the reason that a fitted line is used to find the gradient on such a graph, and not just the two extreme values.

Figure 7.12 Using the fitted line to estimate values

(a) Interpolation   **(b)** Extrapolation

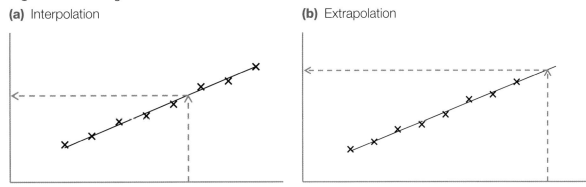

The fitted line may also be extended in order to make estimates of values beyond the range of the original data. Figure 7.12b shows the line being extended to higher values, and a value of y being 'read off' the graph for a value of x that is greater than the original range. This process is called **extrapolation**. For example, a graph showing the extension of a spring against applied force could be extended to find the extension of the spring for a greater force. Care needs to be taken with extrapolation, however, since the linear relationship may not apply outside the data range. In the example of the spring, a point is reached when it becomes 'overstretched' and the extension is no longer proportional to the force.

Extrapolation can also be done by extending the line towards lower values. In such a case, it may be of interest to find out whether it passes through the origin, or, if it does not, to find the value of the intercept on the x-axis or y-axis.

7.6 Origin and intercepts: the meaning of where a fitted line starts

If a straight line on a graph goes through the **origin** then this represents a **proportional** relationship (see Section 5.2 *Proportionality and visual representation* on page 41). Deciding whether the first data point is at the origin, i.e. $(0, 0)$, is important.

Figure 7.13a shows a proportional relationship – it is a graph of current against potential difference for a resistance that follows Ohm's Law. Here, it is apparent that the line *must* go through the origin – if there is no potential difference then there is no current. This could also easily be confirmed by reading these values from the voltmeter and ammeter. For other relationships, we may know that the line must start at the origin, even though in practice there might not be any measurements to show this. Care needs to be taken, however, about making any assumptions about the values at the intercepts, and a line only drawn through the origin when *in principle* it could not be otherwise.

Figure 7.13b shows how the length of a spring varies with force. It is a linear relationship (it obeys Hooke's Law) but it does not pass through the origin, so it is not a proportional relationship. Usually in such a case, the **intercept** on the *y*-axis has a real-world meaning – here, it represents the length of the spring when the value on the *x*-axis (the force on the spring) is zero. In other words, it is its 'normal' length when no force is acting on it to stretch it.

If the original length of the spring is subtracted from all of the data values, this gives the extension of the spring: plotting this against force would be a straight line through the origin, and this a proportional relationship.

In this example, the intercept on the *y*-axis can easily be found by measurement – it is simply the length of the spring with no force. However, in other situations, the intercept cannot be measured directly though it may be found by extrapolation.

Figure 7.13 Lines can meet the axes in different ways

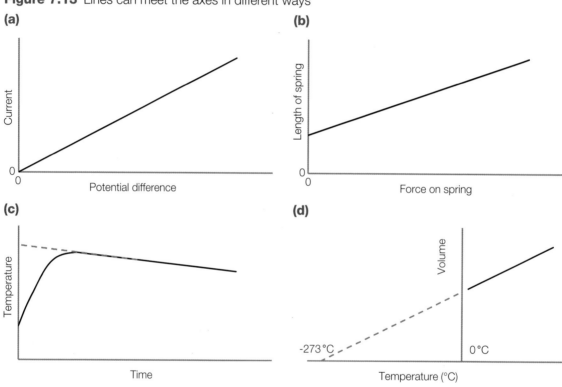

Figure 7.13c represents a graph of the temperature of the reaction mixture during an exothermic chemical change, such as the reaction of zinc with acid in an insulated container. It is not easy to find the 'true' value of the temperature rise, because the reaction takes a little time to complete and during this time energy escapes from the warm reaction mixture. After the initial temperature rise and the completion of the reaction, the mixture starts to cool. Since the container is insulated, the cooling is relatively slow, and approximates to a linear decrease over a small time period. By extrapolating this line backwards, the 'true' temperature rise (i.e. if there had been no cooling) can be estimated from the intercept on the *y*-axis.

An interesting historical use of extrapolation was to estimate the temperature at absolute zero (and this is still a valuable practical activity in post-16 physics). The solid line in Figure 7.13d represents the relationship between the volume of a fixed mass of gas and its temperature. As the gas is cooled, its volume decreases. The theoretical interpretation of this is that the decrease is due to the molecules of the gas moving more slowly. If the molecules stop moving at absolute zero then the volume would approach zero (assuming the volume of the molecules themselves is negligible). Extrapolating the line back to zero volume (here, this means to the point where it meets the *x-axis*), gives a temperature of about −273 °C, which is close to the accepted value.

7.7 When a straight line does not fit all the points

Not every graph has data points that clearly all lie close to a straight line. Two possibilities which may arise are:

- the underlying relationship is linear but there are **outliers**, perhaps due to mistakes in measurement – they may need to be ignored or rechecked
- the underlying relationship is not linear – the line of best fit is a *curve*, not a straight line.

The more data that are collected, the clearer the nature of the relationship becomes. Figure 7.14a shows a graph with just four data points. It is not obvious what the line of best fit might be. Perhaps it is best to draw a straight line close to all of the points (Figure 7.14b), or perhaps treat the final point as an outlier and draw a straight line through the other three (Figure 7.14c), or perhaps it is best to draw a curve close to the points (Figure 7.14d). With only four points, you cannot really decide.

Figure 7.14 It is hard to identify a relationship with a small number of data points

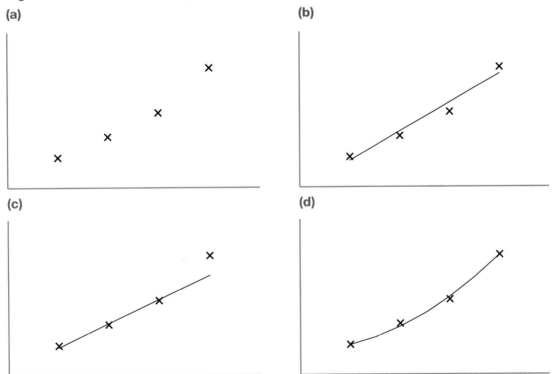

Figure 7.15a shows the original four points but now includes an additional four points to give eight in total. It is now much clearer to see a pattern – it looks like this is a linear relationship but that one of the measurements is an outlier. Figure 7.15b shows a straight line as a line of best fit, using seven of the points and ignoring the outlier.

If a computer is used to find a fitted line, for example on a spreadsheet graph, it may use all eight points including the outlier. The fitted line would then slope more steeply, and by eye would not look like a good fit.

Figure 7.15 Ignoring an outlier when drawing a line of best fit

(a)   **(b)**

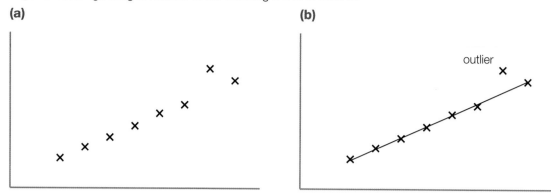

These additional four points were necessary to identify the relationship, but if they had been different then the relationship might have looked very different. Figure 7.16a also shows the original four points but with a different set of four points added. Now, the pattern of data points suggests that the line of best fit should be curved. As before, if the data points are plotted on graph paper, holding it up and looking along the points by eye is a good way of getting a sense of the shape. Drawing good curves by hand needs practice – it can be done using a sweeping movement of the hand with the wrist or elbow as a pivot 'inside' the curve, or by using an instrument known as a 'flexible curve'.

Figure 7.16 A curved line of best fit

(a)   **(b)**

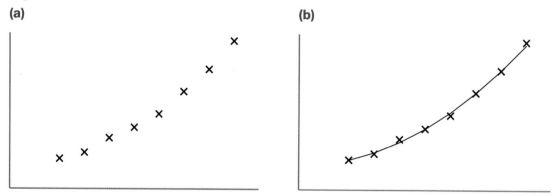

If, instead of a curve, a straight line had been drawn that passed as close to the points as possible then the points in the middle would have been below the line and the ones at each end above. This is a sign that a curve would be a better fit.

Drawing curves is much easier by computer. For example, a formula for a curve could be entered into a spreadsheet but the difficulty may be in finding the correct formula that produces a good fit. In 11–16 science, straight line graphs are more common, though students studying post-16 science come across graphs with curved lines more frequently: in particular, in physics, students need to be able to determine the equations of some non-linear relationships by using logarithmic scales.

8 Looking for relationships: batches and scatter graphs

> **Key words**: population, sample, random sample, batch, variability, stem-and-leaf diagram, histogram, box plot, median, quartile, range, interquartile range, outlier, percentile, scatter graph, variable, correlation, line of best fit.

In the biological sciences, it is quite common to have a data set in which there is an underlying variability in the things being measured. This contrasts with the physical sciences, where variability is more often due to measurement uncertainty. This leads to differences in the way that data are collected (e.g. in thinking about sampling) and the way they are analysed (e.g. in dealing with correlations).

8.1 Different kinds of relationship

Both of the following questions are about how one variable is related to another:

- How does the rate of reaction of zinc with hydrochloric acid relate to temperature?
- How does the lifespan of mammals relate to their heart rate?

Although these look like rather similar types of question, there are important ways in which they are very different.

In the first case, it would be necessary to control all of the variables apart from temperature, such as the amount of zinc, the size and shape of the granules, and the volume and concentration of the acid. However, having done that, we would expect that for every value of the temperature, there would be a unique value of the reaction rate. If the experiment were repeated with *exactly* the same conditions, we would expect that the reaction rate would be *exactly* the same. Of course, the actual values obtained might not be the same because of measurement uncertainty. However, this is due to the limitations in the measuring equipment or our ability to measure, rather than a difference in the phenomenon itself.

The second question is rather more complex. There are different species of mammal, so would it be necessary to collect data for *every* species, or would it be sufficient to make a *selection*? In addition, what does it mean to talk about the lifespan or heart rate for a particular type of mammal, such as a tiger? Different individuals have different lifespans and heart rates. Perhaps taking an average for all tigers? But it would be impossible to collect data on all tigers, so perhaps just a selection?

What this illustrates is that, in designing the collection of data to help answer this kind of question, it is important to consider what to select – in other words, how to *sample*.

8.2   Populations and samples

To discuss the nature of sampling, a simple artificial example will be used. Suppose you have a bag containing a very large number of 1p coins. The composition of 1p coins was changed in 1992, so from that year they were magnetic while before then they were not. Without using a magnet, how could you estimate the proportion of the old non-magnetic coins in the bag? One way would be to check the year of every coin in the bag, but this would take a long time, so better would be to check just a small number at random and make a guess – a process of *sampling*. If you drew out just four coins and found that one of them was pre-1992, you might not be very confident in guessing the proportion in the bag. If however, you drew out 40 coins and found that 10 of them were pre-1992, you would be more confident in saying that the bag might contain around 25% of these coins.

There are two important technical words that can be applied to a situation like this. The collection of all the coins in the bag is known as a **population**. The smaller set of coins selected for checking is known as a **sample**. Note that, in statistics, the term 'population' has a different meaning to that in everyday language – it means a set of things of a similar nature that is of interest as a whole. In everyday language, a 'population' usually refers to a group of people or animals living in a particular area. In a statistical population, however, the 'individuals' could be any kind of object or event.

For example, if the group of interest were the 'population of people in the UK' (an everyday expression) then this would also be a 'population' in the statistical sense. In a factory making computer chips, however, the quality control department might define a 'population' as the group of chips that are made each day, in order that a sample of these can be selected and tested. Not all 'populations' consist of objects: one could think of a 'population' of earthquakes, in which each earthquake is seen as an 'individual'.

'Populations' can apply at different levels. A research study on bees might be interested in all the beehives in a particular area. This collection of beehives is the 'population', and each beehive is an 'individual'. Another study might just look at the worker bees within a single hive. Here, the population is the collection of all the worker bees in that hive, and each worker bee is an individual.

When sampling from a population, it is important that the sample is *representative of the population*. For a collection of 1p coins in a bag, this is fairly easy: coins can just be taken out of the bag *at random*. This means that every coin in the bag has *an equal chance of being selected*, and thus the sample is representative of the population. Such a sample is called a **random sample**. Giving the bag a good shake and not always choosing a coin from the same part of the bag would be a good way of ensuring this.

Another important principle in sampling is the effect of *sample size*. The larger the sample size, the more likely it is that the sample will be *representative* of the population. With samples of just a few coins, there will be a lot of random variation. A sample of a large number of coins is more likely to have a composition similar to that of the whole set of coins. Choosing a small sample means that collecting the data is easier, but with larger samples there is more confidence that the data are representative. In practice, sample size is determined by the balance between these two factors.

Sampling a bag of coins is straightforward but collecting data to answer the question 'How long does a tiger live?' is rather more complex. The 'population of tigers' is harder to define than the 'population of coins'. The 'individuals' in the population would be individual tigers, but which ones? Those that die in a particular year? It is also harder to collect appropriate data and to design sampling procedures that ensure the samples are representative. However, even though the problem is more difficult, the same basic principles of sampling still apply. Having found a 'typical value' for the lifespan of a tiger, this might then be compared to the lifespans of other mammals (polar bears, chimpanzees, grey squirrels, and so on) to see what factors influence the lifespan of different types of mammal. This could involve sampling from a population of 'all types of mammals' in which the individuals would be 'types of mammal'.

8.3 Analysing a batch of data

The table in Figure 8.1 shows the potential lifespan of some selected types (or 'orders') of mammals. The whole data set in fact contains 75 selected mammals listed alphabetically (taken from an article on the internet), but just the first few are given here.

A data set like this is sometimes called a **batch** of data – it contains a set of values about the *same kind of thing*. The values therefore relate to just a *single quantity or variable*. Such data sets are discussed in Chapter 6 *Dealing with variability*, in which it is shown how a **box plot** is a useful visual display for getting a sense of the size and **variability** of the values. Note that the term 'batch' is commonly used in data analysis, though not so much at school level: it is used here, as it is very helpful to have a simple term to describe this kind of data.

Figure 8.1 Potential lifespans of mammals

Mammal	Lifespan (years)
African elephant	60
African giant rat	5
African porcupine	20
Alpine marmot	13
American beaver	19
American bison	23
Asiatic or Indian elephant	78
Australian sea lion	12
Aye-aye	7
Bactrian camel	26
Baikal seal	56
etc.	

This section looks at the techniques for drawing a single box plot for one batch of data. The way in which relationships can be explored by analysing more than one batch of data is discussed later in Section 8.5 *Comparing batches of data* on page 81.

Drawing a box plot requires the values to be put in order of size, so that five summary values can be identified (see Section 6.6 *How much do the values vary?* on page 56). Ordering values is easy to do with a computer spreadsheet but if the values only exist on paper it would take a long time to enter them.

A quick and simple way of organising a large set of data by hand is to construct a **stem-and-leaf diagram**. In this method, the values are first roughly sorted in order of size along a 'stem', and then in a second pass, the individual values (the 'leaves') are put into exact order.

Figure 8.2a shows how to make a start: a vertical 'stem' is drawn with each digit representing 'tens of years' (i.e. 0, 1, 2, 3…8 represent 0, 10, 20, 30…80 years). The final digits of each of the data values are the 'leaves' (with units of 'years'), written in the appropriate positions on the 'stem'.

So, the first value in the list of data is 60 years: to the right of the '6' on the stem is written '0'. The next data value is 5 years, and to the right of the '0' on the stem is written '5'. This is continued for each of the values in the batch, writing each new 'leaf' to the right of the existing ones. Thus, in Figure 8.2a, next to the '1' on the stem, are the digits '3 9' – these represent two data values, 13 years and 19 years.

Figure 8.2b shows the diagram with all 75 values entered. Putting values into groups like this is similar to the construction of frequency tables from discrete data (see Section 3.2 *Using tables to process data* on page 24). The shape of this diagram is similar to the outline of a **histogram** 'on its side'. It shows that there are many values in the intervals 10–19 years and 20–29 years, so this gives a sense of the 'typical' lifespan.

Figure 8.2 Making a stem-and-leaf diagram

(a) The first few values

```
8 |
7 |
6 | 0
5 |
4 |
3 |
2 | 0
1 | 3 9
0 | 5
```

stem: 10 years
leaves: 1 year

(b) All values added

```
8 |
7 | 8 3
6 | 0
5 | 6 0 5 5 0
4 | 0 6 7 2 7 0 9 5
3 | 4 1 0 0 0 2
2 | 0 3 6 8 4 0 0 0 3 0 4 0 0 1 9 7 0 4 0 6
1 | 3 9 2 8 6 7 6 2 7 5 4 5 6 4 6 5 3 5 6 0 4 2
0 | 5 7 9 7 6 6 4 3 5 7 3
```

stem: 10 years
leaves: 1 year

Having ordered the values along the stem, the next step is to put the 'leaves' in order, as shown in Figure 8.3a. Reading from left to right starting at the bottom and going up the stem, the whole batch of values is now completely ordered. (The easiest way to do this is to cross off the digits on the unordered diagram as they are entered on the new ordered diagram.)

Figure 8.3 Ordering and finding summary values from a stem-and-leaf diagram

(a) Ordered

```
8 |
7 | 3 8
6 | 0
5 | 0 0 5 5 6
4 | 0 0 2 5 6 7 7 9
3 | 0 0 0 1 2 4
2 | 0 0 0 0 0 0 0 0 0 1 3 3 4 4 4 6 6 7 8 9
1 | 0 2 2 2 3 3 4 4 4 5 5 5 5 6 6 6 6 6 7 7 8 9
0 | 3 3 4 5 5 6 6 7 7 7 9
```

stem: 10 years
leaves: 1 year

(b) Summary values

```
8 |
7 | 3 [8]
6 | 0
5 | 0 0 5 5 6
4 | 0 0 2 5 6 7 7 9
3 | 0 0 [0 1] 2 4
2 | 0 0 0 0 [0] 0 0 0 0 1 3 3 4 4 4 6 6 7 8 9
1 | 0 2 2 2 3 3 4 [4 4] 5 5 5 5 6 6 6 6 6 7 7 8 9
0 | [3] 3 4 5 5 6 6 7 7 7 9
```

stem: 10 years
leaves: 1 year

The shape of the ordered stem-and-leaf diagram is the same as before but it is now possible to find the summary values for the box plot. These are indicated in Figure 8.3b. The highest and lowest values are easy to identify (78 and 3 years). Since there are 75 values in the whole batch, the **median** is the 38th value (with 37 values below it and 37 values above it): it is 20 years.

To find the upper and lower **quartiles**, the upper and lower halves of the data are each taken as including the median, so they each have 38 values. (Note that this convention is not universal – some sources say that the upper and lower halves are taken without including the median.) Since this is an even number, the 'middle' consists of two values (the 19th and 20th), and a mean is taken of these two. This gives an upper quartile of 31 years (from 30 and 31 years, rounded up from a mean of 30.5 years), and a lower quartile of 14 years (from the values 14 and 14 years).

The five summary values are therefore:

- highest value: 78 years
- upper quartile: 31 years
- median: 20 years
- lower quartile: 14 years
- lowest value: 3 years

From these summary values a **box plot** can be drawn. Figure 8.4 shows the easiest way of doing this by hand. The first step is to draw an appropriate vertical scale and then five horizontal lines corresponding to the summary values, as shown in Figure 8.4a. The next step is to draw the vertical lines to create the box, and connecting the highest and lowest values, as shown in Figure 8.4b. The completed box plot is shown in Figure 8.4c.

Figure 8.4 Drawing a box plot: potential lifespans of mammals

(a) Draw horizontal lines for summary values   **(b)** Connect with vertical lines   **(c)** The completed box plot

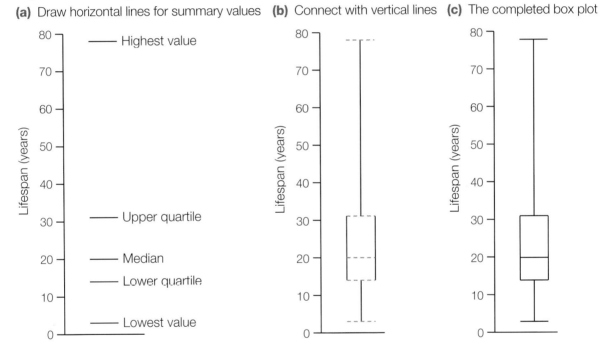

The box plot gives a very clear sense of the variability of mammalian lifespans. While the median value is 20 years, there is a very large variation, with a **range** of nearly 80 years (in fact from 3 to 78 years). As noted in Section 6.6 *How much do the values vary?* on page 56, a better measure of spread is the **interquartile range**, i.e. the range of values included within the box on the box plot. Its value here is 16 years (the difference between the upper quartile and the lower quartile: 30 − 14 years). One half of the mammals in this batch have potential lifespans within this range.

The box plot also shows that the batch of data is *skewed*, with the upper part being 'stretched out' and the lower part being 'squashed together'. This contrasts with the display in Chapter 6 (Figure 6.3) which skewed in the opposite direction.

Note that, in mathematics, pupils may have seen stem-and-leaf diagrams drawn so that values of the stem increase *downwards*. Many books on analysing data adopt the convention that values of the stem increase *upwards*. This is the convention that has been used here, since the stem then matches the scale used for the box plot, and it corresponds to the terms used to describe the summary points (e.g. the highest value is at the top, and so on).

Sometimes, batches of data contain extreme values that are very different from the rest of the values. These are known as **outliers**. For example, a bowhead whale has a lifespan of about 200 years. This was not included in the original batch of data but, if it had been, how could this value be handled? Figure 8.5a shows the box plot of the original batch drawn on a new scale that extends upwards to 200 years. Figure 8.5b shows the box plot redrawn with the upper line extended to the new highest value. Such a plot could be misleading since it may give the impression that there are quite a few types of mammal with lifespans approaching 200 years.

In Figure 8.5c, the original box plot has been drawn, with the new value indicated as an outlier by showing a separate data point labelled 'bowhead whale'. This gives a much better impression of how different this particular type of mammal is from the others in the batch. Such a plot prompts questions to be asked about the reasons for this difference, perhaps related to the whale's size, habitat, diet, and so on.

Figure 8.5 Dealing with outliers: potential lifespans of mammals

(a) Original box plot on the new scale **(b)** New value added as the highest value **(c)** New value added as an outlier

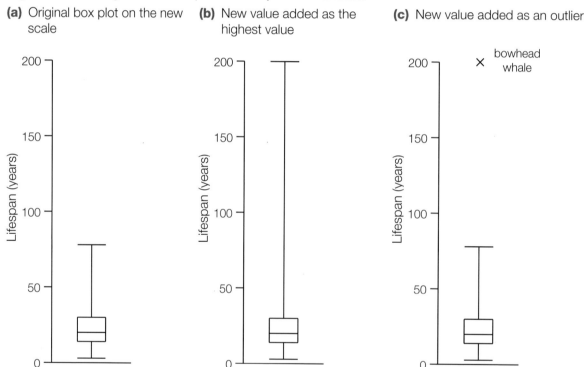

There are no hard-and-fast rules about how to identify what should be considered an outlier. Sometimes there will be values that are very much bigger or very much smaller than the rest of the values and which are clearly outliers; sometimes all of the values in a batch lie fairly close together where there are clearly no outliers. Between these extremes, the decision is a matter of judgement depending on the nature of the data and on what is of interest in the analysis.

Pupils may encounter the term **percentile** in science lessons. This is a similar idea to a *quartile*. You can think of *quartiles* as the values that split a batch of data into *four parts*; in the same way, the *percentiles* are the values that split a batch of data into a *hundred parts*. For example, the World Health Organization has data on the weights of babies at different ages. For baby girls aged 12 months, it gives the value of the 90th percentile as 10.5 kg. This means that 90% of these babies are under this weight, while 10% are over. Since a *median* is the value in the *middle* of a batch, it is the *50th percentile* (50% above and 50% below). The *upper and lower quartiles* correspond to the *75th and 25th percentiles* respectively. Using percentiles can be useful when looking at the way that values are distributed in a batch in a more detailed way than simply using quartiles.

8.4 Dealing with more than one batch of data

The previous section looked at the analysis of a *single **batch*** of data. There are two distinct types of situation where you might be dealing with more than one batch of data. These are illustrated in Figure 8.6.

The first set of data, represented in part in Figure 8.6a, consists of two batches of data: the lifespans for two different types of mammals (rodents and primates). Here, the data are about the *same quantity* for *two different samples.*

The second set of data, represented in part in Figure 8.6b, also consists of two batches of data: the mean heart rates and mean lifespans for selected types of mammals. Here, however, the data are about *two different quantities* related to the *same sample.*

Figure 8.6 Different structures of data

(a) Lifespans for rodents and primates

Rodent	Lifespan (years)
African giant rat	5
African porcupine	20
etc.	

Primate	Lifespan (years)
Aye-aye	7
Chimpanzee	55
etc.	

same quantity
two different samples

(b) Mean heart rates and mean lifespans for different types of mammal

Mammal	Heart rate (beats/min)	Lifespan (years)
Badger	138	11
Cat	120	15
etc.		

two different quantities
same sample

So, although both sets of data consist of two batches, they have *different structures*, and this leads to *different types of questions* that can be asked about the data, for example:

(a) What is the relationship between *lifespan* and *type of mammal* (rodent and primate)?

This is a question about the relationship between a **continuous** *variable* and a **categorical** *variable.*

(b) What is the relationship between *lifespan* and *heart rate* for different types of mammal?

This is a question about the relationship between *two* **continuous** *variables.*

Since these are different types of question involving data of different structures, the data are analysed in different ways. These are discussed in the next two sections.

8.5 Comparing batches of data

Box plots are particularly useful when analysing two or more ***batches*** of data, such as the tables shown in Figure 8.6a, rather than just a single batch. The lifespans of rodents and primates can be compared by drawing a box plot for each of these batches side-by-side, as shown in Figure 8.7.

As for a single box plot, the same questions can be asked about each of these box plots individually: What is the typical lifespan for each of these types of mammal and how much do they vary? In addition, the two batches can be compared. It seems that primates typically live about twice as long as rodents (the median for primates is about twice that for rodents), but there is a lot of overlap. For example, the median value for rodents is a bit higher than the lowest value for primates. This means that a bit over a half of the rodents live longer than the shortest lived primate.

Box plots become even more useful when comparing larger numbers of batches. For example, Figure 8.7 could be extended to include other types of mammal, and this would enable a great deal of data about lifespans to be compared quite easily.

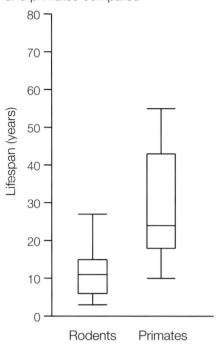

Figure 8.7 Lifespans of rodents and primates compared

8.6 Judging whether a difference is significant

Box plots can be useful when analysing the results of experiments involving a 'control' group and a 'treatment' group. For example, when looking at the effects of a fertiliser on the height of plants, one would expect there to be a variation in the heights of individual plants in both groups. However, the question is whether, *overall*, the plants in the two groups seem to be of different heights, i.e. are the medians of the two groups noticeably different?

If there is no overlap of the 'boxes' (i.e. of the *interquartile ranges*) in the two box plots then it might seem that the batches are very different and the fertiliser had an effect. However, if there is a lot of overlap of the boxes and the medians are quite close then the observed difference may simply be due to chance.

In post-16 biology, students learn about more formal statistical tests of significance to judge whether two batches might really be different or whether the difference could have arisen by chance. Instead of using the median and the interquartile range in the comparison of box plots, these tests use the mean and the standard deviation. However, the principles of these formal tests are similar to how judgements are made by eye using box plots, so representing the data visually in this way forms a good basis for further understanding.

Note that the word '*significant*' has both an everyday meaning and a technical statistical meaning. In everyday language, a *significant effect* is often used to mean a *big effect*. However, in statistics, a significant effect means an effect that is *unlikely to have happened by chance*: it does *not* necessarily indicate that it is a big effect. This is a subtle idea, and certainly goes beyond what pupils need to know in 11–16 science. However, because 'significance' is a term that is encountered in media reports and can cause confusion, it is discussed in outline here.

The idea can be illustrated by thinking about coin tosses (see Section 6.9 *Basic ideas in probability* on page 59). A *fair* coin is one that has an equal probability of landing as a head or a tail. If you tossed a coin 10 times, you might get equal proportions of heads and tails (i.e. 5 of each), but you would not be surprised if you got another outcome (e.g. 7 heads and 3 tails). There is random variation in the outcomes. However, if you tossed the coin many thousands of times, you would expect the proportions of heads and tails to be very close to equal.

Now, suppose you were given an *unfair* or '*biased*' coin, which had an 80% probability of landing heads. If you did not know whether it was biased or not, you might start to suspect after only a few throws that it was not a fair coin. The greater the number of tosses, the more you might believe that it was biased. Eventually you might say that you were 'fairly certain'. You could never be *completely* certain, because an outcome with a very large proportion of heads could still be possible, even though it might be highly unlikely.

Suppose you were given another biased coin, but this time much less so, with just a 51% probability of heads. From a small number of coin tosses, you would not notice that it was biased. By counting a larger number, you might suspect something, but you would need a much larger sample of coin tosses with this coin before you might say you were 'fairly certain'.

What you are really trying to judge here when using a biased coin is whether you might have got these results using a fair coin. If the proportion of heads seems rather too large, you might say that that you are 'fairly certain' that the outcome could not have happened by chance using a fair coin. With some complex calculations, it would be possible to turn 'fairly certain' into a value of a probability; for example, 'there is a 95% probability that this outcome could not have happened by chance'. Another way of saying the same thing is that there is only a 5% probability that the outcome could have happened by chance.

This is the essence of statistical significance. If an outcome is reported as being 'significant at the 5% level', it means that the probability of the outcome happening by chance is only 5% or less. If the reported level of significance is lower (e.g. 1%), it means that there is an even smaller probability that the outcome could have happened by chance.

These ideas are important in experiments involving a 'control' group and a 'treatment' group. Suppose that these were the results of two different studies on fertilisers (with a significance level of 5%):

- With fertiliser A, there was a 7% bigger growth in the treatment group than in the control group. The sample sizes were small and the result was not significant.
- With fertiliser B, there was a 0.1% bigger growth in the treatment group than in the control group. The sample sizes were large and the result was significant.

What these results illustrate is that with small sample sizes you might not get a significant result even with a large effect. With large samples sizes you might get a significant result, even though the effect is small.

So, although the result for fertiliser A is not significant, the difference in the growth seems quite big. It might be worth doing another study with larger samples to see whether the effect might be real, or whether it just happened by chance. For fertiliser B, the result was significant, but the effect is so small that it may not justify the cost of using the fertiliser.

In summary, box plots can be used to compare samples and look at the *sizes of the differences* between them. Statistical tests are used to judge whether the differences are *significant*, in other words, whether it is unlikely they could have occurred by chance.

8.7 Relationships between variables: scatter graphs and correlation

Scatter graphs are useful for looking at the relationship between two ***variables*** of the same sample of individuals. The table shown earlier in Figure 8.6b illustrates this kind of data. The sample consists of selected types of mammals and the quantities are mean heart rate and mean lifespan. Figure 8.8. shows a scatter graph of these data.

This graph suggests that there is *some* relationship between lifespan and heart rate. It seems that, very roughly, as the heart rate of a mammal *increases*, its lifespan tends to *decrease*.

However, it is certainly not an *exact* relationship. It is very different, for example, to the relationship between the mass suspended from a spring and the length of the spring. Here, it is straightforward to control all the variables that affect the length of a spring, and just look at the effect of the suspended mass. For every value of mass, there is a *unique* value for the length of the spring.

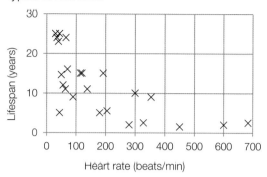

Figure 8.8 A scatter graph of mean lifespan against mean heart rate for some selected types of mammal

For the data on mammals, it is much harder to control all of the variables that could affect a dependent variable. In such a case, it may be possible to see the effect of an independent variable on the dependent variable, but it will be masked by the effects of additional variables that are not controlled. We would *not* expect that for every value of one variable there would be a unique value for the value of the other. There is *variability* in the population.

The distinction between these two examples is also discussed in Section 3.6 *Line graphs and scatter graphs: two related quantities* on page 29. (Note: for the purposes of the discussion in that section, the graph of the mammalian data showed fewer data points.)

One way of explaining the apparent relationship between lifespan and heart rate would be that every mammal tends to have the same fixed number of heart beats in its lifetime. So, if the time between heart beats doubles then the lifespan doubles too.

Figure 8.9 has been drawn to test this idea. The quantity plotted along the horizontal axis is the *time between heartbeats*. This has been calculated from: time between heartbeats in seconds = 60 / heart rate in beats per minute.

Re-expressed in this way, the pattern of the data points now shows a general upward slope. The graph shows that, as the time between heart beats increases, the lifespan increases. The pattern also appears less curved: since it is a bit more 'straight', it suggests that, *very roughly*, if the time between heart beats doubles then the lifespan doubles too. It is clearly not possible to fit a straight line that passes through or close to all of these points, though it can still be useful to draw a line of best fit on a scatter graph like this. (This is discussed later in Section 8.8 *Drawing a line of best fit on a scatter graph* on page 85.)

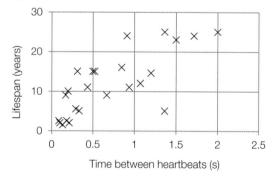

Figure 8.9 A scatter graph of mean lifespan against time between heartbeats for different types of mammal

A **correlation** is a way of expressing the strength of the relationship between two variables. If a scatter graph appears to show that there is a relationship between two variables then we can say that they are *correlated*.

In 11–16 science, pupils only need to be able to talk about correlation qualitatively, but it is worth being aware that it is not just a 'vague' idea. A *correlation coefficient* is a value that can be *calculated* for certain types of data, and students of post-16 biology encounter this quantitative aspect. Calculating a correlation coefficient gives a value between $+1$ and -1. A positive value indicates that, as one variable increases, the other also tends to increase; a negative value indicates that, as one variable increases, the other tends to decrease. A value of 0 indicates no correlation between the variables.

Figure 8.10 shows a series of scatter graphs with varying degrees of correlation. These can be described *qualitatively* using the following terms:

- *positive correlation*: as one variable increases, the other tends to increase as well
- *negative correlation*: as one variable increases, the other tends to decrease
- *no correlation*: there does not appear to be any relationship between the variables
- *strong* or *weak* correlation: to describe how closely the variables appear to be related.

Figure 8.10 Correlations (positive and negative) of different strengths

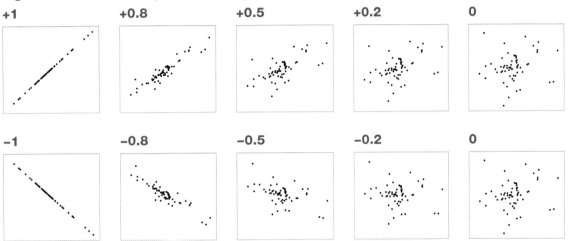

Thus, for these graphs, we could talk about a strong positive correlation between two variables ($+0.8$), a weak negative correlation between two variables (-0.5), or no apparent correlation (0). (Note that the variables in the graphs labelled '$+1$' and '-1' are *perfectly correlated* – they show the points you would expect on straight line graphs.)

An important point that is often made is that *correlation does not imply causation*. If A and B are correlated then it is possible that A causes B, but another possibility is that B causes A. It may be that they are not causally related to one another at all, but that they are both causally related to a third variable C. It is also possible that the apparent correlation between them is just coincidental and happened by chance.

Note that a correlation coefficient is a value that indicates the *size* of an apparent relationship. In more advanced statistical work, a further test needs to be done to judge whether the effect is *significant* or whether it could have arisen by chance. The larger the sample size, the more likely an effect is to be significant.

8.8   Drawing a line of best fit on a scatter graph

The data points on a **scatter graph** are usually, as the name indicates, *scattered*. This is because of the underlying variability in the population concerned. For this reason, the data points do not lie close to any **line of best fit**.

It is, however, still possible to draw a line of best fit on a scatter graph, though it is important to be clear about its meaning. It has a different meaning to the lines of fit discussed in

Chapter 7 *Looking for relationships: line graphs*. The difference arises because of the differences in the nature of the data. For 'line graph' type data, the data points may not all lie on the fitted line because of *measurement uncertainty*. For 'scatter graph' type data, the differences from a fitted line are due to *differences between individuals in a population*. The distinction between these two different kinds of variability is discussed in Section 6.1 *Where does variability come from?* on page 50.

Figure 8.11 shows the same scatter graph as in Figure 8.9, but here a line of best fit has been added. A straight line has been chosen, since the distribution of data points does not look particularly 'curvy' The criteria for fitting the line are that it should have similar numbers of points above and below the line and the gradient of the line should reflect the distribution of the points (as discussed in Section 7.4 *Lines of best fit: linear relationships*

Figure 8.11 A line of best fit on a scatter graph

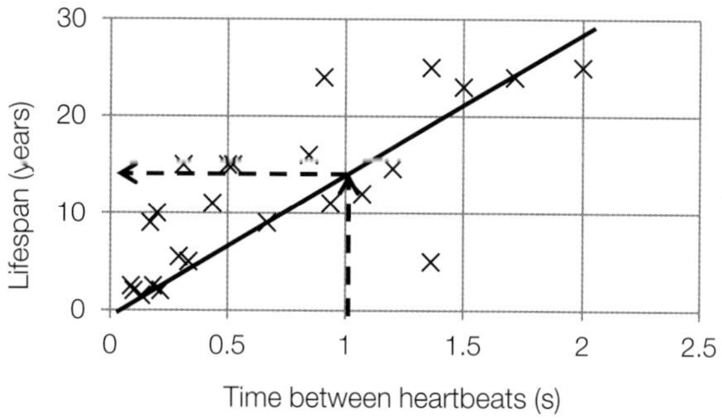

on page 69). Deciding on where to draw the line when the points are very scattered involves more judgement than when they are close to a line. It is not so easy to decide on which is the 'best' line.

The straight line on the graph can now be used to make *estimates* or *predictions*. For example, suppose you were asked what lifespan a mammal might have if it had a 'time between heartbeats' of 1 second. The dotted lines in Figure 8.11 show that the best guess would be about 14 years. This is only a rough estimate but it is a better guess than if we had no information at all about the time between heartbeats. It is not a perfect guess since the data points do not lie exactly on the line because of the variability in the population.

In this example, a *straight* line was chosen as the line of best fit because the distribution of the data points suggested it (the formal term for such a line is a *regression line*). In mathematics, pupils are generally given data for which a straight line is a good fit; in science, pupils may need to decide whether a straight line or a curve is the best fit. For example, in the scatter graph shown in Figure 3.10, a curve would be a better fit for the data than a straight line.

9 Scientific models and mathematical equations

> **Key words:** equation, algebraic equation, formula, expression, variable, constant, coefficient, brackets, order of operations, subject of a formula, proportional, directly proportional, constant of proportionality, linear relationship, linear equation, inversely proportional, exponential relationship, inverse square relationship, line graph, rate, intercept, gradient, tangent, area under the line (on a graph).

In science, a graph shows a relationship between quantities in the real world. Some graphs are produced by collecting and plotting experimental data. However, some graphs are representations of how we might imagine the world to be, based on certain sets of assumptions or 'scientific models'. Underlying the behaviour of these models are the mathematical equations that breathe life into our imagined worlds.

9.1 Equations, formulae and expressions

Before going further, it is useful to clarify the meaning of a number of terms about which there is sometimes confusion. Central to this chapter will be a discussion of the manipulation and graphical representation of **equations** (also referred to as **algebraic equations**). An equation is a mathematical statement that indicates the equality of the expressions to the left and right of the equals ($=$) sign. Figure 9.1 shows some examples of equations.

All of these equations contain variables but they differ in their nature. In equations (a), (b) and (c) the variables are *abstract*, but in equations (d), (e) and (f) the variables represent *physical quantities*. An equation that shows the relationship between physical quantities is called a **formula**. So, every formula is an equation, though not every equation is a formula.

Note that although equation (d) looks different to equation (a) because it uses *words* (density, mass and volume) rather than *symbols* (x and y), this is *not* what makes it a formula. Equations (e) and (f) both represent the same formula for calculating kinetic

> **Figure 9.1** Examples of equations
>
> (a) $y = \dfrac{x}{3} - 1$
>
> (b) $y = mx + c$
>
> (c) $2x^2 + 5x - 3 = 0$
>
> (d) $\text{density} = \dfrac{\text{mass}}{\text{volume}}$
>
> (e) $\text{kinetic energy} = \frac{1}{2} \times \text{mass} \times \text{velocity}^2$
>
> (f) $E_k = \frac{1}{2}mv^2$

energy. What makes both of them formulae is that the variables, whether expressed as words or as symbols, relate to physical quantities. (The advantages and disadvantages of using words or symbols are discussed in Section 9.5 *The real-world meaning of a formula* on page 93.)

Pupils should also be aware that the terms *formula* and *equation* have additional meanings in chemistry: a chemical *formula* (e.g. H_2O) is a symbolic way of showing the relative numbers of atoms in a substance, while a chemical *equation* is a symbolic representation of the rearrangement of those atoms that occurs in a chemical reaction. The idea of 'balance' applies to both types of equation: in an algebraic equation the *values* on each side are equal, and in a chemical equation the *numbers of atoms* on each side are equal.

An **expression** is a combination of numbers and variables that may be evaluated – expressions do *not* contain the equals (=) sign. (Note that 'evaluating an expression' means finding its numerical value – a very different meaning to 'evaluating a science investigation'.) So, the equations listed above are not themselves expressions, but they do *contain* expressions. Examples of expressions are shown in Figure 9.2.

Figure 9.2 Examples of expressions

$$\frac{x}{3} - 1 \qquad \frac{x}{3} \qquad 3x^2 - 5x - 2 \qquad 5x \qquad \frac{mass}{volume} \qquad velocity^2 \qquad \tfrac{1}{2}mv^2$$

Notice that, in an algebraic expression such as $5x$, the convention is that there is no multiplication sign between the '5' and the 'x', even though this means '5 multiplied by x'. However, for a word expression, the multiplication sign is included for clarity, for example $\tfrac{1}{2} \times mass \times velocity^2$.

When such an expression is expressed symbolically, the multiplication signs are omitted and it is written as $\tfrac{1}{2}mv^2$ (writing $\tfrac{1}{2} \times m \times v^2$ could be confusing as $\times$ could be mistaken for x). Since these symbols do not have a space between them, all physical quantities are represented by just a single letter (e.g. m for mass, v for velocity, and so on). Additional information about a variable that needs to be included can be indicated using a subscript or superscript (e.g. E_k). Note that this contrasts with units, which often have more than one letter (e.g. cm or kg) and are always written with spaces in between each unit.

Similarly, using the division sign ($\div$) explicitly is not the only way to represent division. The following expressions are the same:

$$mass \div volume \qquad mass\ /\ volume \qquad \frac{mass}{volume}$$

The third way of representing division in an expression is generally preferable because it makes the relationship clearer to see. This is particularly the case when there are more than two values or variables in the expression.

9.2 Variables, constants and coefficients

Expressions may include letters that represent *variables*, *constants* and *coefficients*, and it is also useful to clarify the meaning of these words, particularly as they are used differently in mathematics and science.

An example of a **variable** is represented by the letter x in this **equation**:

$$y = \frac{x}{3} - 1$$

It is a variable because it can take on a range of values. In this example, as the value of x varies, y also varies, and so y is a variable too.

In science, the term 'variable' is also used in this sense, being represented by a letter or word(s) in an algebraic equation. For example, in the following equation, *mass* and *volume* are both variables and could each take on a range of values:

$$\text{density} = \frac{\text{mass}}{\text{volume}}$$

These values would give a range of values for *density*, and so this too is a variable. However, the term 'variable' is used in a broader sense in science. It can be used to refer to *any* factor that could be varied in a scientific investigation, whether or not it forms part of an algebraic equation. Such equations represent only **quantitative** variables, and often variables are **qualitative** (categorical). Quantitative variables (continuous or discrete) may be identified at the start of an investigation, to find out whether there is a relationship that can be expressed as an algebraic equation; even if none is found, they are still referred to as 'variables'.

Note that in published texts the letters that represent variables are shown in *italics*, but not the letters that represent units. So, mass may be represented by the letter m, while the abbreviation for metre is m. This distinction is not made when writing by hand.

An example of the use of a **constant** in mathematics is illustrated in the equation:

$$y = mx + c$$

This is the general equation of a straight line, where m and c represent constants (m is the gradient of the line and c is the intercept). Substituting different numerical values for m and c gives different straight lines; for example, $y = 2x + 1$ represents one particular straight line, and $y = 3x + 2$ represents another one.

In a scientific investigation, we may refer to '*keeping a variable constant*' (i.e. the control variable). For example, the current through an electrical resistor depends on two variables – its resistance and the voltage applied across it. In an investigation, we could look at the effect on the current of changing the resistance while keeping the voltage constant, or changing the voltage while keeping the resistance constant.

The word 'constant' is also used in science to refer to those physical quantities that really are 'constant', and where they always have the same value whenever they are used. Examples of such physical constants include the speed of light in a vacuum (about $3 \times 10^8 \, \text{m s}^{-1}$) and the Avogadro constant (about $6.02 \times 10^{23} \, \text{mol}^{-1}$), Note that although these are *constants*, this does not mean they are just numbers – they are values that have *units*.

The word **coefficient** can easily be confused with *constant*. In the expression $3x^2$, the coefficient of x^2 is '3', and in the expression $5x$, the coefficient of x is '5'. The term does not just apply to numerical values; so, for example, in the expression $\frac{1}{2}mv^2$, as well as saying that $\frac{1}{2}$ is the coefficient of mv^2, we could say that $\frac{1}{2}m$ is the coefficient of v^2. In science, however, the word is also often applied to a value that is constant for a particular material under certain conditions but that is different for different materials (e.g. the coefficient of expansion or the coefficient of thermal conductivity).

9.3 Operations and symbols

An **expression** may contain symbols that represent *operations*. Two common operations are *addition* and *subtraction*, and these are represented by the familiar plus (+) and minus ( ) signs. *Multiplication* and *division* are also common operations, though the signs that can be used to represent them ($\times$ and $\div$) are often not used explicitly (see Section 9.1 *Equations, formulae and expressions* on page 87).

A subtle point, but one that becomes much more important for post-16 science, is that the plus (+) and minus (−) signs are actually used in two distinct ways. For example, take these two expressions:

$$5-3 \qquad -3$$

In the first of these, the minus symbol is acting as an *operator* – it is telling us to *subtract* the value 3 from the value 5. In the second of these, it is telling us that this is a *negative value*. The same applies to the 'plus' sign, which has different meanings in the following two expressions.

$$5+3 \qquad +3$$

Note that while the 'minus' symbol is *always* used to indicate a negative value, often we do not explicitly use the 'plus' symbol to indicate a positive value, and simply write '3'.

This distinction is essential in understanding expressions that involve the addition and subtraction of positive and negative values, for example:

$$(+6)+(-4)-(-2)$$

One area of 11–16 science where pupils may encounter such expressions is the use of vectors to describe and analyse motion (see Sections 10.5–10.8).

In an **equation**, the equals (=) sign indicates that the expressions on each side are equal. There are a number of other useful symbols that are used to compare expressions, and these are shown in Figure 9.3.

The first three symbols (=, >, <) are clear-cut in their meaning and are probably the ones most commonly encountered.

The next two symbols (≥, ≤) can be useful in defining class intervals (see Section 6.4 *Displaying larger sets of values* on page 53). For example, the phrase 'those pupils whose height is 150 cm or above but less than 160 cm' can be expressed more simply as $150 \,\text{cm} \leq \text{height} \leq 160 \,\text{cm}$.

An approximate value can be indicated by using the symbol '~'; for example, approximately 3 g can be written as ~3 g. The symbol '≈' is a combination of ' =' and '~' so, instead of writing 'mass = ~3 g', it is simpler to write 'mass ≈ 3 g'.

Figure 9.3 Examples of symbols used to compare expressions

$y = x$	'y equals x' or 'y is equal to x'
$y > x$	'y is greater than x'
$y < x$	'y is less than x'
$y \geq x$	'y is greater than or equal to x'
$y \leq x$	'y is less than or equal to x'
$y \approx x$	'y is approximately equal to x'
$y \gg x$	'y is much greater than x'
$y \ll x$	'y is much less than x'

The last two symbols (≫, ≪) are not common in 11–16 science. One example of their use might be in a situation where one is handling an algebraic equation that includes an expression such as $m_A + m_B$, where these represent the masses of two objects, A and B. If the mass of A is very much bigger than the mass of B then the expression might be simplified, by assuming that the mass of B can be ignored and that the total mass can be taken as just the mass of A. This can be represented as:

$$\text{since } m_A \gg m_B, \text{ then } m_A + m_B \approx m_A$$

9.4   Calculations using formulae: order of operations

Many of the **formulae** that pupils encounter in 11–16 science involve just one operation. For example, density can be calculated by dividing mass by volume – a single operation. In formulae where there is *more* than one operation, it is essential that they are carried out in the correct order.

Here is a simple example to illustrate this:

$$4 + 2 \times 3$$

A different value is obtained depending on whether the addition or multiplication is done first, as shown in Figure 9.4.

It might seem common sense that the first of these is correct since the operations are done in order from left to right, and the result should be 18. Indeed, if this series of numbers and symbols were entered into most calculators, the result given would be in fact be 18. However, this is *not* the convention that has been adopted in mathematics, in which *multiplication takes precedence over addition*. The correct value is therefore 10.

Figure 9.4 Which order is correct?

(a) Addition first	**(b)** Multiplication first
$4 + 2 \times 3$	$4 + 2 \times 3$
6×3	$4 + 6$
18	10

Pupils need to be aware of how to handle the **order of operations** in order to be able to make calculations and to rearrange formulae. The explanations for these will be given and then summarised at the end of this section.

In an **expression** involving only addition and subtraction, the operations are carried out in order from left to right (Figure 9.5a). A different order, for example, from right to left, may give a different (and incorrect) result (Figure 9.5b).

Figure 9.5 Addition and subtraction only

(a) Left to right (correct)	**(b)** Right to left (incorrect)
$4 + 3 - 2 - 1$	$4 + 3 - 2 - 1$
$7 - 2 - 1$	$4 + 3 - 1$
$5 - 1$	$4 + 2$
4	6

In an expression involving only multiplication and division (using $\times$ and $\div$ signs), these operations are also carried out in order from left to right (Figure 9.6a). As before, a different order may give an incorrect result (Figure 9.6b). However, this expression could be written more clearly and less ambiguously by avoiding the use of the $\div$ sign (Figure 9.6c). The top and bottom expressions are evaluated first before the final division.

Figure 9.6 Multiplication and division only

(a) Left to right (correct)	**(b)** Right to left (incorrect)	**(c)** Clearer (and correct)
$3 \times 4 \div 2 \div 2$	$3 \times 4 \div 2 \div 2$	$\dfrac{3 \times 4}{2 \times 2}$
$12 \div 2 \div 2$	$3 \times 4 \div 1$	
$6 \div 2$	3×4	$\dfrac{12}{4}$
3	12	3

If an expression contains a combination of these operations then multiplication and division take precedence over addition and subtraction (Figure 9.7a). If, however, a calculation requires that an addition or subtraction should take precedence then this can be done using **brackets**. (Figure 9.7b). Evaluating expressions in brackets takes precedence over *all* other operations.

Figure 9.7 Handling brackets

(a) With no brackets	**(b)** With brackets
$10 - 2 \times 3$	$(10 - 2) \times 3$
$10 - 6$	8×3
4	24

It would be possible to add brackets to $10 - 2 \times 3$ giving the expression $10 - (2 \times 3)$, and it would still give a value of 4. The brackets, though, are unnecessary since multiplication already has precedence. Even though they are not needed, it would not be incorrect to use the brackets here, so it may be better to include brackets when in doubt or for additional clarity.

Pupils should also be able to handle calculations involving *indices* (i.e. those that include expressions of the form x^n in which x is raised to the power of n). Indices take precedence over all of the operations discussed so far (addition, subtraction, multiplication, division) except brackets. Figure 9.8a illustrates the precedence of an index over a multiplication, while Figure 9.8b shows how brackets take precedence over an index.

Figure 9.8 Handling indices

(a) Index takes precedence	**(b)** Brackets take precedence
2×3^2	$(2 \times 3)^2$
2×9	6^2
18	36

To summarise these ideas, a rather contrived example of a calculation is shown in Figure 9.9 to illustrate the **order of operations**.

Figure 9.9 Order of operations

The original expression:	$4 + 2 \times (5 - 2)^2$
Expressions inside *brackets* are evaluated first, to give:	$4 + 2 \times 3^2$
Next *indices* are evaluated, to give:	$4 + 2 \times 9$
Then *multiplication* and *division*, to give:	$4 + 18$
Finally, *addition* and *subtraction*, to give:	22

This convention is summarised in the widely used mnemonic BIDMAS (**B**rackets, **I**ndices, **D**ivision/**M**ultiplication, **A**ddition/**S**ubtraction). An alternative form of the mnemonic is BODMAS (where O represents **O**rder or 'to the power **O**f').

For simplicity, all of these examples have involved only numbers but the same conventions about the order of operations apply to the manipulation of algebraic equations. Furthermore, in scientific formulae the values have units; making sure that the handling of the units makes sense provides an additional check on the correct sequence of operations (e.g. one cannot add unlike units).

The use of calculators needs care in making sure that the operations are done in the correct order. It is often safer to write down intermediate values – indeed, in scientific calculations, these intermediate values are often useful to calculate in any case as they have a real-world meaning.

9.5 The real-world meaning of a formula

It is helpful to think of a **formula** not just as a mathematical equation but as something that 'tells a story' about the real world. For example, take the formula that defines speed:

$$\text{speed} = \frac{\text{distance}}{\text{time}}$$

As well being able to substitute values and to calculate a result, pupils should be able to interpret what this formula is saying and to check that this makes sense. The formula shows that speed is **directly proportional** to distance: so, in real-world terms, the greater the distance that someone walks in a certain time, the greater their speed. It also shows that speed is **inversely proportional** to time: so, the greater the time that someone walks a certain distance, the lower their speed. Pupils should be able to see that these real-world interpretations of the formula make sense.

The formula above defines the relationship between *three* variables. Knowing the values of any *two* of the variables means that the *third* variable can be calculated. The formula allows *speed* to be calculated but rearranging it gives formulae that allow *distance* and *time* to be calculated (how to rearrange formulae will be discussed in subsequent sections of this chapter):

$$\text{distance} = \text{speed} \times \text{time}$$

$$\text{time} = \frac{\text{distance}}{\text{speed}}$$

Again, in these formulae, pupils should be able to identify directly proportional and inversely proportional relationships, and to relate the formulae to real-world interpretations.

There are many formulae used in 11–16 science that involve three variables that are related in this way, i.e. through direct and inverse proportion. Other examples include:

$$\text{density} = \frac{\text{mass}}{\text{volume}}$$

$$\text{chemical amount (in moles)} = \frac{\text{mass of substance}}{\text{molar mass}}$$

$$\text{force exerted on spring} = \text{spring constant} \times \text{extension}$$

Note that the underlying form of all these formulae is the same. Although the last formula looks different from the others (the right-hand side shows two variables multiplied together), the first two formulae could also each be rearranged to show two variables multiplied together. Each of the formulae here, however, is shown in the way it is most commonly written.

Note also that some formulae represent *definitions* whereas others represent *empirical relationships*. For example, the first formula is a *definition*: it represents the way that density is defined. In a definition, the relationship between the variables is *exact*. The last formula, by contrast, represents an *empirical relationship* (Hooke's Law), which is an approximation to the way that real springs behave.

When pupils first start to use scientific formulae, it is generally better to express these using *words* rather than symbols for the variables, since this helps to emphasise the real-world meaning. As they get older, it is appropriate that they also become familiar with symbolic formulae. These have a number of advantages. They are shorter to write down, making them easier to manipulate and rearrange. The symbolic form may also be easier to remember: in the two versions for kinetic energy below, the symbolic one is visually more recognisable, as well as its sound ('a-half-em-vee-squared') being more memorable.

$$\text{kinetic energy} = \tfrac{1}{2} \times \text{mass} \times \text{speed}^2 \qquad E_k = \tfrac{1}{2}mv^2$$

The following sections discuss the techniques that can be used to rearrange formulae. Pupils need to be able to rearrange a formula if the quantity that they are trying to calculate is not 'on its own' on the left-hand side. The discussion starts with the simplest kind of formula, involving only addition and subtraction, before moving on to those involving multiplication and division.

9.6 Rearranging formulae involving addition and subtraction

Suppose that in a class of pupils there are 13 boys and 15 girls. It is not difficult to work out that the total number of pupils in the class is 28. More formally, one could represent this as a '*formula*' for calculating the number of pupils in a class (Figure 9.10).

> **Figure 9.10** A simple formula
>
> $$\text{number of pupils} = \text{number of boys} + \text{number of girls}$$
> $$= 13 + 15$$
> $$= 28$$

Now suppose that, in a different class, we want to work out the number of girls knowing that the total number of pupils is 30 and the number of boys is 14. Again, it is not difficult to work out the result – there must be 16 girls – but the above formula does not give this directly. In order to do this, the formula needs to be *rearranged* so that 'number of girls' becomes the **subject of the formula**, i.e. it is 'on its own' and by convention on the *left* of the equals sign. Using our common sense about the situation, we should be able to write down a rearranged formula for working out the number of girls (Figure 9.11).

> **Figure 9.11** Rearranging the formula
>
> $$\text{number of girls} = \text{number of pupils} - \text{number of boys}$$
> $$= 30 - 14$$
> $$= 16$$

However, most formulae are not as easy to rearrange as this, so it is important for pupils to understand the general principles for rearranging formulae, in order to apply these to any situation. There are really just two principles – for simplicity, these will be illustrated using only numbers at first but they apply in exactly the same way to formulae involving variables. Figure 9.12 uses the example of '2 + 3 = 5': the value of the expression on the left is 5 and that on the right is 5 – they are equal.

The first principle is that the sides of an equation can be *swapped* – an equation shows that the expression on the left is equal to the expression on the right, so it does not matter in which order they are written. The left and right sides are still equal if the sides are swapped (Figure 9.12a).

The second principle is that the left and right sides of an equation remain equal if the *same operation is performed on each side*. For example, the sides are still equal to each other if the *same value is added* to each side: Figure 9.12b shows that, if '2' is added to each side, they remain equal (each has a value of 7). The same applies if the *same value is subtracted* from each side: if 3 is subtracted from each side, they are both equal to 2.

> **Figure 9.12** Principles for rearranging equations
>
> **(a)** Swapping sides
>
> 2 + 3 = 5
> the sides remain equal if the sides are swapped:
> 5 = 2 + 3
>
> **(b)** Doing the same thing to each side
>
> 2 + 3 = 5
> the sides remain equal if the same operation is performed on each side:
> 2 + 3 + 2 = 5 + 2
> 2 + 3 − 3 = 5 − 3

Returning to the original formula for working out the total number of pupils in a class, how could we rearrange this so that 'number of boys' is the subject of the formula (i.e. on the left)? Figure 9.13 shows how the two principles for rearranging equations can be applied to do this.

> **Figure 9.13** Applying the principles
>
> The original formula:
>
> number of pupils = number of boys + number of girls
>
> So that 'number of boys' is on the left, swap sides:
>
> number of boys + number of girls = number of pupils
>
> In order to have just 'number of boys' on the left side, subtract 'number of girls' from each side:
>
> number of boys + number of girls − number of girls = number of pupils − number of girls
>
> This gives:
>
> number of boys = number of pupils − number of girls

Writing out the steps like this might seem a bit laborious (though if symbols were used for the variables rather than words, it would be both quicker to write as well as clearer to see). However, manipulating equations in this way emphasises the *understanding of the principles*, which is important for equations where it may not be so straightforward. After gaining in confidence and understanding, some pupils might begin to take shortcuts, but it is not recommended that these should be taught as this can lead to misconceptions. It is better to teach in a way that focuses on the principles in order to develop understanding.

After rearranging a formula, it is always important to check it and to think about whether it *makes sense* (see Section 9.5 *The real-world meaning of a formula* on page 93).

9.7 Rearranging formulae involving multiplication and division

Many *formulae* in 11–16 science involve three variables that are *directly proportional* or *inversely proportional* to each other. For example, the formula that defines density is:

$$\text{density} = \frac{\text{mass}}{\text{volume}}$$

Suppose that you know the density and the volume of something and want to use the formula to calculate its mass. It needs to be rearranged so that *mass* is the **subject of the formula**. Rearranging such formulae is something that pupils find quite challenging.

Working first with just numbers may help pupils to explore and get a better sense of the different ways of expressing the relationship, for example:

$$\frac{12}{6} = 2$$ could be rearranged as $2 \times 6 = 12$ or $6 = \frac{12}{2}$ and so on.

Rearranging the formula for density uses the same two principles as in the previous section on addition and subtraction. Figure 9.14 shows how the principles of swapping sides and carrying out the same operation on both sides can be used to make *mass* the subject of the formula.

Figure 9.14 Rearranging to make mass the subject of the formula

The original formula:

$$density = \frac{mass}{volume}$$

So that 'mass' is on the left, swap sides:

$$\frac{mass}{volume} = density$$

To remove volume from the left side, multiply each side by 'volume':

$$volume \times \frac{mass}{volume} = volume \times density$$

On the left side, 'volume' cancels out (since volume ÷ volume = 1), and so the rearranged formula becomes:

$$mass = volume \times density$$

Suppose instead that we want to rearrange the original formula so that *volume* is the subject of the formula. This is shown in Figure 9.15. As always, pupils should check the meaning of a rearranged formula: does it make sense that volume is directly proportional to mass and inversely proportional to density? Would the formula be obviously wrong if these were reversed (so that density was divided by mass)?

Again, confident pupils might take shortcuts, but it is recommended that teaching should always emphasise an understanding of the principles by carrying out all of the steps.

9.8 Rearranging other formulae

Most **formulae** in 11–16 science involve only addition, subtraction, multiplication and division. One exception is the formula for kinetic energy. Suppose we want to rearrange this to make 'speed (*v*)' the **subject of the formula**.

$$E_\mathrm{k} = \tfrac{1}{2}mv^2$$

Figure 9.15 Rearranging to make volume the subject of the formula

The original formula:

$$density = \frac{mass}{volume}$$

Here, swapping sides is not a helpful first step to get 'volume' on its own on the left side. Instead, multiply each side by 'volume':

$$volume \times density = volume \times \frac{mass}{volume}$$

On the right side, 'volume' cancels out (since volume ÷ volume = 1):

$$volume \times density = mass$$

In order to remove 'density' from the left side, divide each side by 'density':

$$\frac{volume \times density}{density} = \frac{mass}{density}$$

On the left side, 'density' cancels out (since density ÷ density = 1), and so the rearranged formula becomes:

$$volume = \frac{mass}{density}$$

This is a bit more difficult than the previous examples, but again illustrates the same two principles for rearranging equations (Figure 9.16).

Figure 9.16 Rearranging to make velocity the subject of the formula

The original formula:

$$E_k = \tfrac{1}{2}mv^2$$

So that v is on the left, swap sides:

$$\tfrac{1}{2}mv^2 = E_k$$

To remove the $\tfrac{1}{2}$, multiply both sides by 2:

$$mv^2 = 2E_k$$

Divide both sides by m:

$$v^2 = \frac{2E_k}{m}$$

Taking square roots of each side gives the final formula (this is another example of 'doing the same thing to both sides'):

$$v = \sqrt{\frac{2E_k}{m}}$$

Another example, this time involving reciprocals, is the formula for the total resistance of two resistors in parallel:

$$\frac{1}{R_{total}} = \frac{1}{R_1} + \frac{1}{R_2}$$

There are a number of different ways that this could be rearranged so that R_{total} is the subject, though they all give the same result. Figure 9.17 shows one way of doing this.

Figure 9.17 Rearranging to make total resistance the subject of the formula

Original formula:

$$\frac{1}{R_{total}} = \frac{1}{R_1} + \frac{1}{R_2}$$

Multiply both sides by $R_1 R_2 R_{total}$

$$\frac{R_1 R_2 R_{total}}{R_{total}} = R_1 R_2 R_{total}\left(\frac{1}{R_1} + \frac{1}{R_2}\right)$$

This simplifies to:

$$R_1 R_2 = R_2 R_{total} + R_1 R_{total}$$

Rearrange the expression on the right-hand side:

$$R_1 R_2 = R_{total}(R_1 + R_2)$$

Swap sides:

$$R_{total}(R_1 + R_2) = R_1 R_2$$

Divide both sides by $(R_1 + R_2)$:

$$R_{total} = \frac{R_1 R_2}{R_1 + R_2}$$

Although this example is considerably more demanding than the previous examples, it still uses the same two principles for rearranging equations.

9.9 Calculations without formulae

The idea that a *formula* tells a 'story' also works the other way round. It is useful to remember formulae, but knowing things about the way the world works means that formulae can often be worked out. In addition, it may not always be necessary to use a formula. This section gives two examples to illustrate this.

Example 1

What is the mass of $20\,cm^3$ of aluminium (density $= 2.7\,g/cm^3$)? One way of answering this question would be to write down the relevant formula (from memory or looking it up) and then substitute the values. Alternatively, it can be done by reasoning about the situation:

(1) $1\,cm^3$ of aluminium has a mass of $2.7\,g$

(2) $20\,cm^3$ of aluminium has a mass of $20 \times 2.7\,g = 54\,g$

Step (1) is using the original information to explain what the density implies. In step (2), the reasoning is that 20 times the volume of aluminium will have 20 times the mass.

Example 2 (which requires more steps):

What chemical amount (in moles) of water molecules are there in $10\,g$ of water (molar mass $= 18\,g/mol$)?

(1) $18\,g$ of water contains $1\,mol$ of water molecules

(2) $1\,g$ of water contains $1/18\,mol$ of water molecules

(3) $10\,g$ of water contains $10/18\,mol$ of water molecules $= 0.56\,mol$

Step (1) is using the original information to explain what the molar mass implies. In step (2), the reasoning is that $1/18$ of the mass of water will have $1/18$ of the chemical amount (in moles). Finally, in step (3), similar reasoning means that 10 times the mass of water has 10 times the chemical amount.

This technique is an example of *proportional* reasoning. Since it involves a step in which you calculate the value of one variable when the other has a numerical value of 1, it is known as the *unitary method*.

9.10 Use of 'calculation triangles'

A quite common technique for avoiding the need to rearrange formulae is the use of 'calculation triangles'. Many teachers dislike this method as they see it as a way of getting the right answer in an examination without any need for real understanding. Pupils often like the method for precisely the same reason, and some teachers may therefore feel under an obligation to use the method. The technique is generally regarded as poor practice because it does not encourage pupils to develop their understanding of these kinds of relationship.

An example of its use can be illustrated with the following question: What is the current through a resistance of $10\,\Omega$ if a potential difference of $3\,V$ is applied across it?

If this calculation is done using equations then the first step is to write down the formula that relates the three variables:

$$\text{potential difference} = \text{current} \times \text{resistance}$$

The next step is to rearrange this so that current is the subject of the formula:

$$\text{current} = \frac{\text{potential difference}}{\text{resistance}}$$

Substituting the values for potential difference (3 V) and resistance (10 Ω) gives the current as 0.3 A.

How to do this with a calculation triangle is shown in Figure 9.18. The relationship between potential difference (V), current (I) and resistance (R) is represented in Figure 9.18a. Covering up any one of the symbols in this triangle gives the expression required to calculate it. For example, to calculate the value of the current, the symbol 'I' is covered up (Figure 9.18b). Substituting the values in the expression for the remaining symbols (Figure 9.18c) gives the required answer.

Figure 9.18 Using 'calculation triangles' does not encourage understanding

    (a) A calculation triangle   **(b)** Covering up the symbol 'I' ...   **(c)** ... gives the expression for calculating it

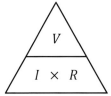
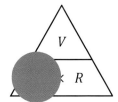

$$\frac{V}{R}$$

Of course, in order to use a 'calculation triangle', a pupil first needs to write it down with the three symbols in the correct positions. One of the problems with this method is that this is not the way that formulae are shown in scientific texts, nor the way the pupils are expected to remember them. So, remembering the correct calculation triangle requires at least as much work as remembering the formula.

Even once the triangle is written down, the use of this representation focuses more on just getting the right answer. As discussed in Section 9.5, pupils should always be thinking about the real-world meaning of a formula.

There are a variety of formulae in school science but calculation triangles have limited applicability and pupils may not always appreciate this. If they try to use triangles for equations that involve addition and subtraction, they will get incorrect results. Relying on their use means that pupils are not developing the skills to become fluent in rearranging different types of equations.

On a positive note, the visual form of a calculation triangle does emphasise that the three variables are related to each other, and that any of the variables can be calculated from the other two. A formula shows just one of these calculations. If teachers do feel pressurised into using them, they should be used as a complement to the understanding of the nature and meaning of equations rather than as a replacement.

9.11 Mathematical equations and relationships in science

Many relationships in science can be modelled by a small number of mathematical **equations**. Figures 9.19–9.24 show the most common of these, and how they can be represented on **line graphs**. Each figure shows the relevant mathematical equation (expressed using x and y), along with an example of where such a relationship can be found in science.

Figure 9.19 shows a **proportional** relationship (or a **directly proportional** relationship). This is a particularly common relationship in science and is discussed in detail in Chapter 5 *Working with proportionality and ratio*. The graph shows a straight line that passes through the **origin**.

An example of this is a resistor that follows Ohm's Law, in which the current through it is proportional to the potential difference applied across it. This means that, for example, if the potential difference is doubled then the current also doubles.

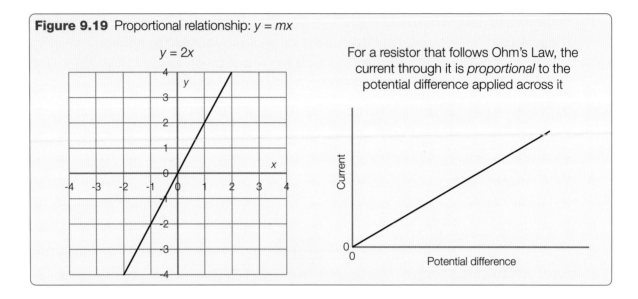

Figure 9.19 Proportional relationship: $y = mx$

$y = 2x$

For a resistor that follows Ohm's Law, the current through it is *proportional* to the potential difference applied across it

Figure 9.20 shows a **linear relationship**. This is similar to a proportional relationship in that the graph shows a straight line, but here it does not pass through the origin. An example of this is Hooke's Law, in which the total length of a spring increases linearly with the force exerted on it. This means that equal increases in force produce equal increases in the length of the spring. The **intercept** on the vertical axis is the length of the spring when the force on it is zero, i.e. the 'normal' length of the spring.

Note that the general equation for a proportional relationship is often written as $y = kx$, where k is the **constant of proportionality**. In Figure 9.19 it is written as $y = mx$, in order to emphasise the similarity to the general equation for a linear relationship, $y = mx + c$, as shown in Figure 9.20. A proportional relationship is a special case of a linear relationship in which $c = 0$. Since c is the intercept on the vertical axis, this means that, when it is zero, the line passes through the origin.

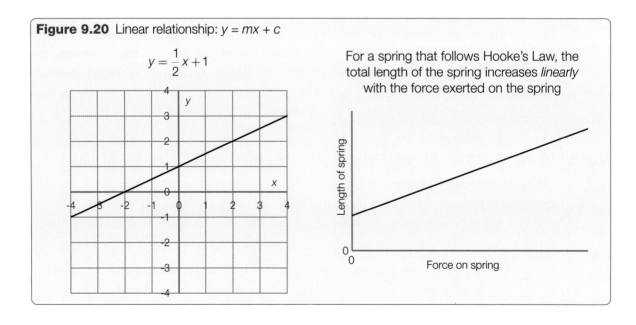

Figure 9.20 Linear relationship: $y = mx + c$

$y = \dfrac{1}{2}x + 1$

For a spring that follows Hooke's Law, the total length of the spring increases *linearly* with the force exerted on the spring

In Figure 9.20, the *length* of the spring is plotted on the vertical axis; subtracting its 'normal' length from these values gives the *extension* of the spring. Plotting these values would 'shift the line down' so that it passes through the origin. Instead of a linear relationship, this would then represent a proportional relationship. Extension is proportional to force and when there is no force the extension is zero.

Figure 9.21 shows a *square* relationship. Note here that the graph on the left includes both positive and negative values of *x*, while the science example just shows the right side of the graph representing only positive values. The example here is the relationship between the kinetic energy of an object and its speed (for which negative values would have no real-world meaning). This relationship is not linear: the line on the graph is curved, and it shows that the kinetic energy increases more rapidly than the speed.

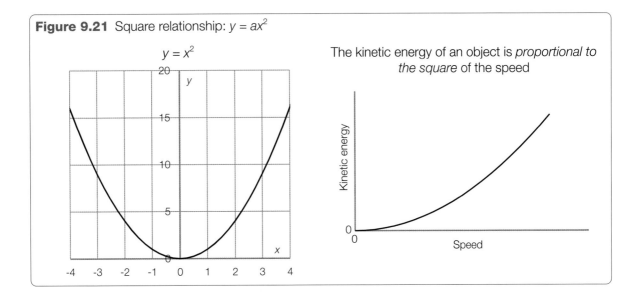

Figure 9.21 Square relationship: $y = ax^2$

Figure 9.22 shows an ***inversely proportional*** relationship (or an *inverse* relationship). This kind of relationship is also discussed in Chapter 5 *Working with proportionality and ratio*. Again, note that the graph on the left shows both positive and negative values of *x*. An example in science is the relationship between the volume and pressure of a fixed mass of gas. The inverse relationship means that, for example, if the pressure is *doubled* then the volume is *halved*. Note that, as the pressure is increased, the volume gets smaller and smaller but never reaches zero (it would if the pressure were infinite but this is impossible). On the graph, therefore, the curve gets closer and closer to the horizontal axis but never actually meets it. (The technical term for the line to which a curve is tending is an *asymptote*.)

Figure 9.23 shows an ***exponential relationship***. The rising curve on the graph looks similar to the curve for the square relationship but, in fact, an exponential curve rises much more rapidly than a square relationship does. Exponential relationships are found whenever the rate of change of a quantity is proportional to the quantity itself. For example, if the numbers of bacteria double every hour then, starting with 1 bacterium, there would be just 2 at the end of the first hour. In the fifth hour, there would be 16 at the start which would rise to 32. This leads to very rapid growth – if they continue to increase like this then there would be over 16 million at the end of 24 hours. In reality, there would be limits to the growth of increasing numbers of bacteria so, unlike the graph on the left, the curve cannot go on rising forever.

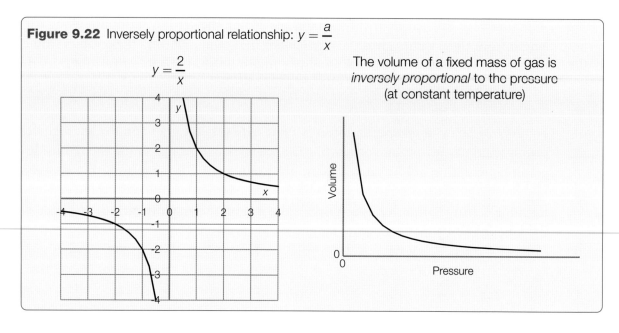

Figure 9.22 Inversely proportional relationship: $y = \dfrac{a}{x}$

$y = \dfrac{2}{x}$

The volume of a fixed mass of gas is *inversely proportional* to the pressure (at constant temperature)

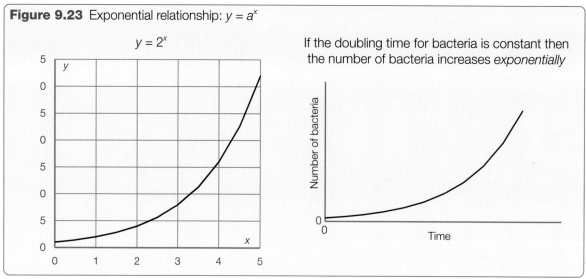

Figure 9.23 Exponential relationship: $y = a^x$

$y = 2^x$

If the doubling time for bacteria is constant then the number of bacteria increases *exponentially*

In the case of bacterial growth, the exponent x in the equation $y = a^x$ is greater than 1 and the change is an example of *exponential growth*. In radioactive decay, the rate of decay is proportional to the amount of radioactive material remaining but in this case the exponent is *smaller* than 1. The graph slopes downwards, rapidly at first and then slowly approaching the horizontal axis. This is an example of *exponential decay*.

Figure 9.24 shows an ***inverse square relationship***. This is similar in shape to the inverse relationship but the decrease towards the horizontal axis is rather steeper in this case. An example is the way that the intensity (or irradiance) of light from a lamp decreases as you move away from the lamp. Again, the curve approaches the horizontal axis but never meets it. So, as you move away from a lamp, the light intensity falls quite steeply but theoretically would never drop to zero, no matter how far you moved away.

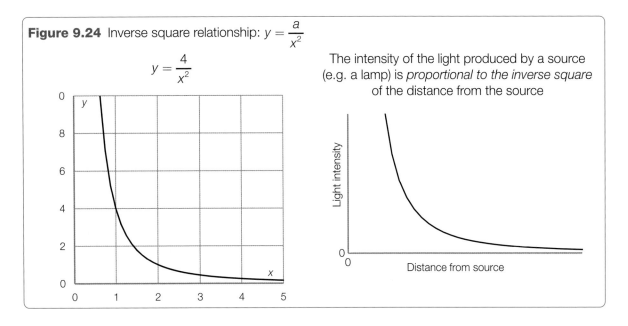

Figure 9.24 Inverse square relationship: $y = \dfrac{a}{x^2}$

$$y = \frac{4}{x^2}$$

The intensity of the light produced by a source (e.g. a lamp) is *proportional to the inverse square of the distance from the source*

9.12 Graphs of quantities against time: gradients

A **line graph** shows the relationship between two variables. The way the line rises or falls tells us about how fast or slow the change is – i.e. about the **rate** of change of one variable with another. This section looks at line graphs that show changes over *time* (i.e. time is the variable on the horizontal axis); such line graphs tend to be the easiest to interpret because the way we talk about the horizontal axis on a graph often reflects a sense of 'one thing happening after another' in going from left to right. However, the principles discussed here apply to any kind of a line graph.

Figure 9.25 shows two graphs that represent a bath filling with water. In Figure 9.25a, the bath starts with 50 litres of water (the **intercept** on the vertical axis) and reaches 200 litres after 10 minutes. The straight line shows that the bath is filling up at a *constant rate*. In Figure 9.25b, the bath also starts with 50 litres and reaches 200 litres after 10 minutes, but here it is not filling up steadily – the *rate changes*. At the beginning it fills up more quickly, and then slows down towards the end.

Figure 9.25 Graphs of quantities against time: a bath filling with water

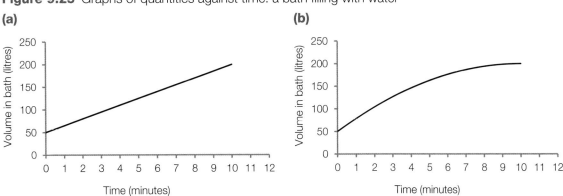

(a)

(b)

The **gradient** of the line represents the rate of change. Pupils need to be able to calculate the gradient of a line on a graph plotted by hand on graph paper. Figure 9.26a shows how this is done for a straight line graph. Finding the gradient involves finding the value for the change in the quantity on the horizontal axis and the corresponding change in the quantity on the vertical axis, and then dividing one by the other. The changes in the quantities can be found by drawing a triangle, as shown in Figure 9.26a. It is always best to draw the triangle as large as possible (so that the values can be measured more accurately), while at the same time choosing a convenient value along the horizontal (in this case 10 minutes).

If pupils have drawn a line of best fit, they need to understand why drawing a triangle on the fitted line to calculate a gradient is better than just using the two extreme data points. Each of the data points is subject to measurement uncertainty, so the fitted line is the 'best guess' of the nature of the relationship.

The change along the vertical axis is 150 litres (200 litres − 50 litres). The gradient is then found by dividing the vertical value by the horizontal value:

$$\text{gradient} = \frac{150 \text{ litres}}{10 \text{ minutes}} = 15 \text{ litres/minute}$$

The gradient represents the rate at which water is flowing into the bath. In this example, the flow rate is constant: 15 litres are added to the bath every minute.

In the other example, shown in Figure 9.26b, the gradient of the curve changes over time. For example, the rate of change is greater at 3 minutes than at 7 minutes. This can be emphasised by drawing a **tangent** to the curve at each of these points. The gradient of the tangent at 3 minutes is steeper than the one at 7 minutes.

Figure 9.26 Finding the value of a rate by calculating the gradient of a line

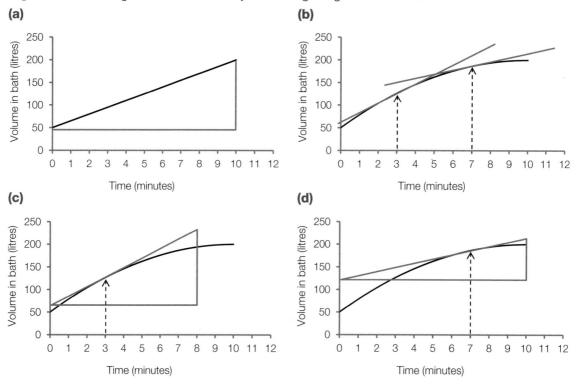

To draw a tangent by hand at a particular point on the curve, it is best to first mark this point on the curve. A ruler can then be positioned so that it passes through this point, with the curve on either side of this point sloping away from the ruler.

The gradients of these tangents can be calculated in the same way as before, by drawing a conveniently sized triangle, as shown in Figures 9.26c and 9.26d. The values of the gradient work out, in fact, at 21 litres/minute and 9 litres/minute respectively.

Drawing a tangent to a curve and calculating the gradient gives an *instantaneous* rate of change, i.e. the rate at that particular instant in time. It is *not* the same as the *average (mean)* rate up to that point in time. This would be found by dividing the total change in volume by the total time elapsed. It is important to make this distinction between *instantaneous* rate of change and *average* rate of change.

A similar distinction is important in the case of a graph of potential difference (*V*) against current (*I*) for a non-ohmic component, such as a filament bulb. Since it does not follow Ohm's Law, it is not a straight line graph but a *curve*. The resistance (*R*) of the component at any point is found by dividing the *value* of *V* by the *value* of *I* ($R = V/I$). However, it is sometimes believed, incorrectly, that it is the *gradient* at a point on the curve that gives the resistance (*R*) at that point. This is *not* the resistance but is the *instantaneous rate of change* of *V* with *I* (the *change* in *V* divided by the *change* in *I*). For a resistor that follows Ohm's Law, the graph is a straight line passing through the origin: calculating the gradient of the line gives the same value as calculating *V*/*I* for any pair of points along it.

9.13 Graphs of rates against time: area under the line

The previous section showed how it was possible to calculate a gradient at any point along a line. Suppose that this is done for a series of points along each of the lines in the graphs shown earlier in Figure 9.25. These gradients represent the **rate** of change of the volume of water in the bath at each of these points in time (i.e. the rate of flow of the water). If these values are then plotted against time, the **line graphs** obtained are shown in Figure 9.27.

The first of these graphs (Figure 9.27a) shows a horizontal straight line. This represents a *constant rate of flow* of water, with a value of 15 litres/minute.

The second graph (Figure 9.27b) also shows a straight line but here it slopes downwards. The flow rate starts at a high value (30 litres/minute) and then drops to zero after 10 minutes. Since it is a *straight line*, it means that the *rate of flow* decreases at a *constant rate* over this period of time. What we are talking about here is a *rate of change of a rate of change* – quite a complex idea! This idea is quite commonly encountered in 11–16 science, though in a different context: an *acceleration* is a rate of change of a rate of change of displacement (see Section 10.7 *Gradients of lines on speed–time and velocity–time graphs* on page 116).

Figure 9.27 Graphs of rates against time: a bath filling with water

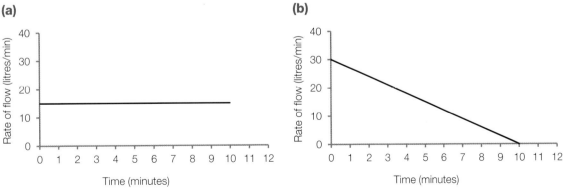

The previous section also showed how it is possible to use a graph showing a *quantity* plotted against *time* to calculate a *rate of change of the quantity*. It is also possible to go 'backwards'. In other words, it is possible to use a graph showing a *rate of change of a quantity* plotted against *time* to calculate the *quantity*.

Suppose we want to find the volume of water added to the bath between 3 minutes and 7 minutes. The graph in Figure 9.28a shows this period of time for the 'constant flow' bath. From this we can see that water flowed at a rate of 15 litres/minute for 4 minutes. To obtain the volume of water added in this time, we multiply these two values together, giving a total of 60 litres.

One way of thinking about this calculation is that it is the same as calculating the area of the shaded rectangle, i.e. the **area under the line** on the graph. In fact, for any line graph where the *line* represents the values for a *rate of change of a quantity*, the *area under the line* represents the value of the *quantity*.

Figure 9.28 Finding the value of a quantity by calculating the area under a line

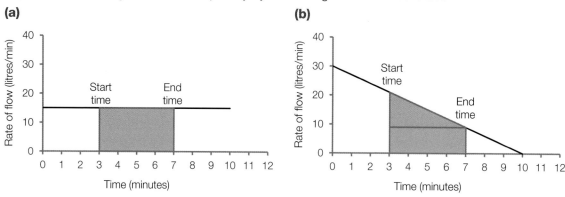

This idea, of calculating the area under the line on a graph also applies to the bath that is being filled with a *changing* rate of flow of water. This is shown in Figure 9.28b. Here, it is not quite so straightforward to calculate the area because it is not a rectangle.

One way of doing this is to split the area into two parts – a rectangle with a triangle on the top. The areas of these can then be found separately and added together. (The area of a right-angled triangle is one half of the area of a rectangle with the same base and height; see Section 10.2 *Length, area and volume* on page 108 for the formula to calculate the area of a right-angled triangle.)

Another way of doing this is to multiply the *mean* rate of flow by the time. On this graph, the mean rate of flow is the value at 5 minutes (it is the mean of the values at 3 and 7 minutes). This is equivalent to calculating the shape of the whole shaded area, which is a *trapezium*; pupils learn about calculating the area of a trapezium in mathematics.

Both of the graphs in Figure 9.28 are straight line graphs. If the graph had shown a *curve* then the area under the curve would still have the same meaning, though finding it would be less straightforward. One technique, if the graph is plotted on graph paper, is to estimate the numbers of large and small grid squares that are under the curve, and add up the areas.

Talking about baths filling with water is a concrete way of thinking about these ideas. In 11–16 science, however, pupils more often use calculations of the 'area under a line' in the context of *velocity–time graphs* (or speed–time graphs). These are discussed in more detail in Section 10.8 *Area under the line on speed–time and velocity–time graphs* on page 118.

10 Mathematics and the real world

Key words: mass, weight, area, volume, square, cuboid, cube, scale drawing, scale factor, linear dimension, cross-sectional area, surface area, surface area : volume ratio, radius, diameter, circumference, scalar, vector, distance, displacement, speed, velocity, gradient, distance–time graph, displacement–time graph, speed–time graph, velocity–time graph, area under the line (on a graph).

In school mathematics teaching, real-world contexts may be used to help pupils understand abstract ideas as well as how they can be applied. Some of these contexts are the same as those that are also studied in school science. This section looks at such overlaps, in particular those related to the fundamental quantities of mass, length and time.

10.1 Mass and weight

In everyday life, it is quite common to talk about the *weights* of things measured in *grams* (g) or *kilograms* (kg). These are the units shown on familiar items such as kitchen scales or bathroom scales, and it is usual to think of these as devices for weighing things.

In science, however, an important distinction is made between the **mass** of an object and the **weight** of an object: the *kilogram* is a unit of *mass*, and *weights* are measured in *newtons* (N). It is not that science is correct and everyday language is wrong, but that words are used in different ways in different contexts. Pupils need to understand these differences.

Weight may be the more intuitive concept – heavy objects weigh a lot and are hard to lift up. Weight can be defined scientifically as the gravitational force exerted on an object, and most pupils know that things weigh less on the Moon than on Earth because there is 'less gravity'. However, if an object is taken from the Earth to the Moon, there is still the same amount of 'stuff' or matter in it, even if it weighs less; its mass is a measure of the amount of matter in the object.

Why is this distinction important in science? The following two equations illustrate the difference:

kinetic energy $= \frac{1}{2}mv^2$ (where m = mass and v = velocity)

weight $= mg$ (where m = mass and g = gravitational field strength)

Kinetic energy depends only on an object's mass and velocity. For example, an object of mass 2 kg travelling at 3 m/s has a kinetic energy of 9 J ($\frac{1}{2} \times 2$ kg $\times$ (3 m/s)^2). Its kinetic energy is 9 J whether it is travelling on Earth, on the Moon or in space, since its mass is the same in all of these places.

The weight of an object depends on the gravitational field strength. The value of this is slightly different in different places on the Earth (e.g. in Birmingham it is 9.817 N/kg and in Los Angeles it is 9.796 N/kg), but the average is about 9.81 N/kg. On the Moon, it is much less, at about 1.63 N/kg. A person with a mass of 75 kg would have a weight on Earth of about 736 N (75 kg × 9.81 N/kg) but a smaller weight on the Moon of about 122 N (75 kg × 1.63 N/kg).

Although the weight of this 75 kg person would be slightly different in different places on Earth, the difference is very small (e.g. about 1.002 times heavier in Birmingham than Los Angeles). It is therefore convenient to assume that the gravitational field strength is constant across the Earth, and to treat the weight of an object as being proportional to its mass.

This is the justification for the everyday practice of talking about weights measured in kilograms. It would sound odd and out of place in a shop to talk about 'finding the mass' of some apples rather than 'weighing them'. However, in the school science laboratory, pupils using a balance calibrated in grams should always talk of it as measuring mass.

In school mathematics, it is common to see the term mass used in its scientific sense, but it is possible that pupils may come across books and resources that use the term weight in its everyday sense. In science, it is essential to understand the distinction between mass and weight, as well as being aware of how the terms may be used outside the science classroom.

10.2 Length, area and volume

In mathematics lessons, pupils are likely to have learnt about calculating **areas** and **volumes** for a variety of two-dimensional and three-dimensional shapes, including the use of units and how to convert from one unit to another. In 11–16 science, pupils also come across calculations of areas and volumes, though for a more limited range of shapes.

For two-dimensional shapes, the following **formulae** are used to calculate the areas of a rectangle, a **square** (the special case of a rectangle with equal sides), and a right-angled triangle:

area of a rectangle $= a \times b$ (where a and b are the lengths of the sides)

area of a square $= a^2$ (where a is the length of the side)

area of a right-angled triangle $= \frac{1}{2}bh$ (where b is the base and h is the height)

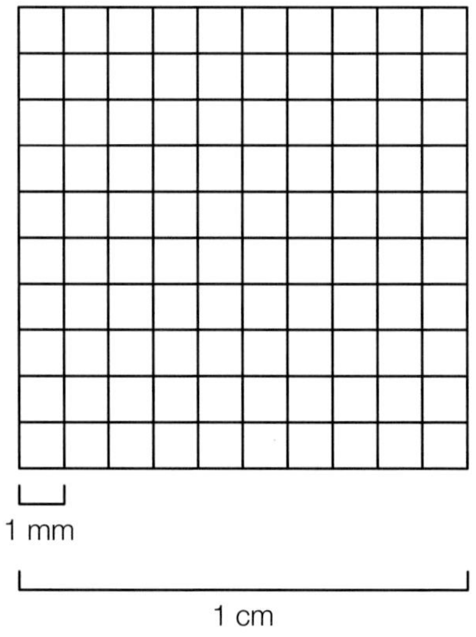

When calculating the area of a rectangle, the *units* of the length for each side should be the same. Common units of measurement of length are millimetres (mm), centimetres (cm), metres (m) and kilometres (km). The corresponding units of area are square millimetres (mm^2), square centimetres (cm^2), square metres (m^2) and square kilometres (km^2).

The area of a rectangle of 2 cm by 3 cm is 6 cm^2. What is this area expressed in square millimetres (mm^2)? An easy mistake to make is to think that, since 1 cm = 10 mm, 6 cm^2 = 60 mm^2. Figure 10.1 makes the point that a square with a side of 1 cm contains 100 (10 × 10) squares with a side of 1 mm. Thus, 6 cm^2 600 mm^2.

Similarly, in 1 m^2 there are 10 000 cm^2 (100 cm × 100 cm), and in 1 km^2 there are 1 000 000 m^2 (1000 m × 1000 m).

Figure 10.1 An area of 1 cm^2 equals 100 mm^2

1 mm

1 cm

For three-dimensional shapes, the following **formulae** are used to calculate the volumes of a **cuboid** (a shape for which each face is a rectangle) and a **cube** (the special case of a cuboid with equal sides):

$$\text{volume of a cuboid} = a \times b \times c \text{ (where } a, b \text{ and } c \text{ are the lengths of the sides)}$$

$$\text{volume of a cube} = a^3 \text{ (where } a \text{ is the length of the side)}$$

When calculating the volume of a cuboid, the units of the length for each side should be the same. Common units of volume are cubic millimetres (mm^3), cubic centimetres (cm^3), cubic decimetres (dm^3) and cubic metres (m^3).

Figure 10.2 A volume of $1\,dm^3$ equals $1000\,cm^3$

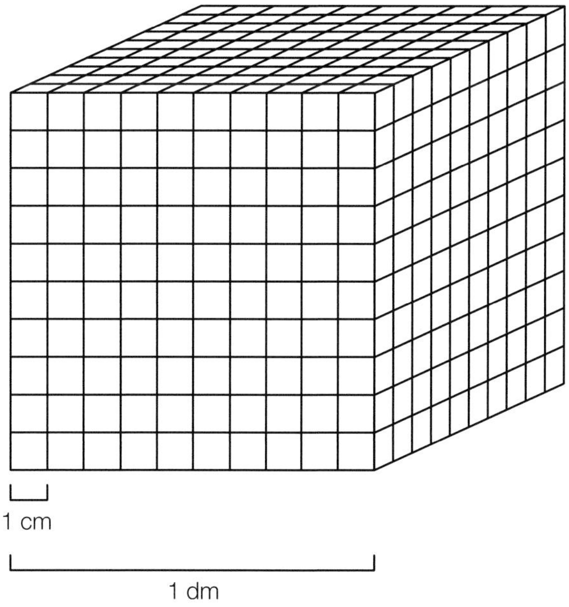

In everyday life, the volumes of liquids, such as milk or soft drinks, are usually given in millilitres (ml) or litres (l). These units are still encountered in science for liquid measurement, though their use is historical. The accepted units are cubic centimetres ($1\,cm^3 = 1\,ml$) and cubic decimetres ($1\,dm^3 = 1\,l$). As the name suggests, there are 1000 millilitres in 1 litre; Figure 10.2 illustrates that in $1\,dm^3$ there are $1000\,cm^3$ ($10\,cm \times 10\,cm \times 10\,cm$).

Similarly, in $1\,m^3$ there are $1000\,dm^3$ ($10\,dm \times 10\,dm \times 10\,dm$), and $1\,000\,000\,cm^3$ ($100\,cm \times 100\,cm \times 100\,cm$).

1 cm

1 dm

Pupils should understand that the *dimensions* of the unit indicate what quantity is being measured; for example, cm^2 (*two* dimensions) is a measure of *area* while mm^3 (*three* dimensions) is a measure of *volume*.

10.3 Scale factor, cross-sectional area and surface area

A **scale drawing** is one in which all of the dimensions of the original object are multiplied by a constant **scale factor**. (Scale factors are discussed in Section 5.9 *Scale drawings and images* on page 48.) For example, in Figure 10.3a, a rectangle with sides of 1 cm and 2 cm has an area of $2\,cm^2$. Re-drawing this with a scale factor of 2 (i.e. doubling the length of each side, called the **linear dimensions**) gives a rectangle with sides of 2 cm and 4 cm and an area of $8\,cm^2$. Doubling the linear dimensions increases the area not by 2 but by 4 times. (The scale factor is 2, so the area changes by 2^2 times.)

Similarly for a three-dimensional object, doubling the linear dimensions does not result in a simple doubling of the volume. Figure 10.3b shows a cuboid of dimensions $1\,cm \times 1\,cm \times 2\,cm$, giving a volume of $2\,cm^3$. Doubling the linear dimensions of the object gives a volume of $16\,cm^3$ ($2\,cm \times 2\,cm \times 4\,cm$). Thus, doubling the linear dimensions increases the volume not by 2 but by 8 times. (The scale factor is 2, so the volume changes by 2^3 times.)

Figure 10.3 Effects of scaling

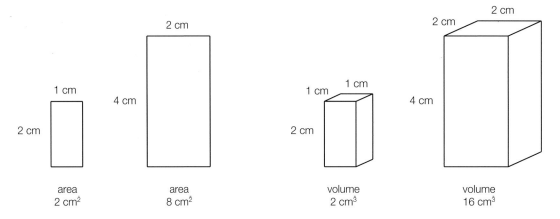

In summary, when an object is scaled:

change in the linear dimensions ∝ scale factor

change in the area ∝ (scale factor)^2

change in the volume ∝ (scale factor)^3

The examples given in Figure 10.3 relate to a *doubling* of the linear dimensions (a scale factor of 2) but the same principles apply to other scale factors. For example, if the linear dimensions are *trebled* (a scale factor of 3) then the area increases by 9 times (3^2) and the volume increases by 27 times (3^3).

These scaling effects are important in many areas of science, particularly biology. For example, it explains why the legs of an elephant are much thicker relative to its body size than those of a mouse. Figure 10.4 shows how doubling the linear dimensions of a cuboid affects its volume and its **cross-sectional area**. The volume increases *8 times*, but the cross-sectional area only *4 times*.

Figure 10.4 Cross-sectional area and scaling

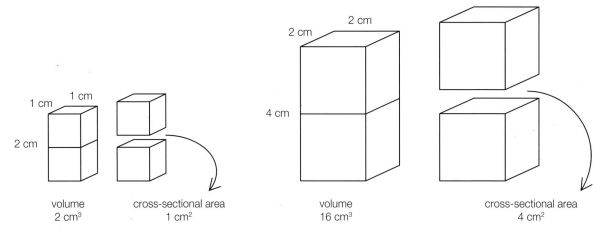

The strength of an animal's legs is related to their cross-sectional area, while the weight of the animal is related to its volume. If a mouse were to be scaled up in size, its legs would not be strong enough to support its weight. It is because weight increases faster than strength that an elephant's legs are relatively much thicker.

Another similar example is the limit placed on the size of a biological cell. The surface area of a cell must be sufficient for substances to diffuse into and out of the cell fast enough.

Figure 10.5 shows the effect of doubling the size of a cuboid on its volume and on its **surface area**. As in the previous example, the volume increases *8 times*, but the surface area only *4 times*.

This idea is usefully expressed in terms of the **surface area : volume ratio**. Since the change in the area is proportional to (scale factor)^2 and the change in the volume is proportional to (scale factor)^3, this means that the change in the surface area : volume ratio is inversely proportional to the scale factor. That is, *doubling* the linear dimensions leads to a *halving* of the surface area : volume ratio.

If a biological cell is scaled up in size, its surface area : volume ratio gets smaller, and it is this that puts a limit on the size of a cell. Substances are not able to move in and out through the surface of the cell fast enough for its volume.

Figure 10.5 Effect of size on surface area : volume ratio

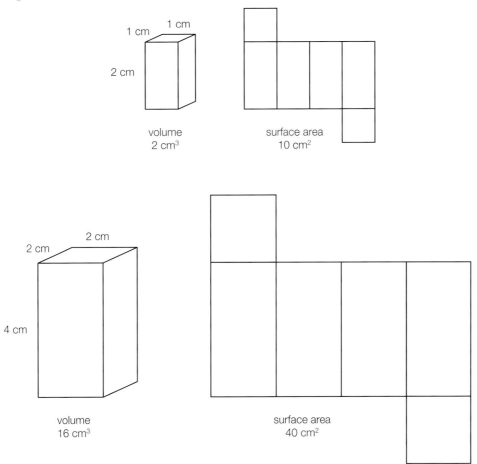

The surface area : volume ratio is also affected by the *shape* of an object. If you have eight cubes each of 1 cm^3, there are various ways of arranging them. Whichever way they are arranged, they always have the same total volume (8 cm^3) but the surface areas may be different. To have the smallest surface area, they need to be arranged in a cube (2 × 2 × 2), as shown on the left of Figure 10.6. Counting the number of squares on each face shows that this has a total surface area of 24 cm^2. The arrangement with the largest surface area (8 × 1 × 1) is shown on the right. This has a surface area of 32 cm^2.

Figure 10.6 Effect of shape on surface area : volume ratio

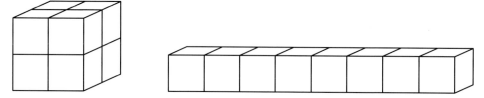

An example of this in the real world is how to keep warm in cold conditions. It is better to try to roll up into a ball, thus reducing your surface area from which heat can escape. (Note that a sphere has a smaller surface area than a cube of the same volume. A sphere is the shape that has the smallest possible surface area : volume ratio.)

Human perception is not good at comparing the volumes of objects. The drawing in Figure 10.7 represents two objects, the second of which is twice the volume of the first. It is not easy to judge this by eye. Talking about 'doubling the size of an object' is ambiguous if it is not made clear whether this is referring to the linear dimensions, the area or the volume.

Figure 10.7 It is difficult to compare the volumes of objects

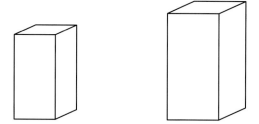

On a bar chart it is relatively easy to compare the sizes of the bars because we only need to pay attention to the *length* of the bars. Some 'informal' graphical displays replace the bars with different sized 3D representations of an object that are related to the quantity being plotted (pictograms). For example, electricity consumption may be represented by different sized light bulbs. Because of the difficulties in making the comparisons, such displays can be misleading (and indeed may sometimes be used to mislead deliberately). Using 3D representations in bar charts is best avoided.

10.4 Circles and spheres

Modelling biological aspects of the world using squares and cubes may be convenient, but in nature such shapes are less common than circles and spheres. However, calculations involving these (which always involve π) are not so easy to handle and are not much used in 11–16 science, though pupils should be familiar with the formulae for doing such calculations from their mathematics lessons.

Mathematically, a circle and a sphere are defined in terms of the set of points that are a fixed distance (the **radius**) from the centre. However, for a real object, such as a coin or a ball bearing, it is the **diameter** that is more easily measured. So, while in mathematics the formulae used are usually based on the radius, in science the context determines whether it is more useful to use radius or diameter.

In the following formulae, the letter r represents the radius:

diameter of a circle $= 2r$

circumference of a circle $= 2\pi r$

$$\text{area of a circle} = \pi r^2$$

$$\text{surface area of a sphere} = 4\pi r^2$$

$$\text{volume of a sphere} = \tfrac{4}{3}\pi r^3$$

An important point about such formulae is that the power to which r is raised (r, r^2 or r^3) is a clue to the nature of what is being calculated:

- the **diameter** and **circumference** of a circle are **linear dimensions** and are proportional to r

- the *area* of a circle and the *surface area* of a sphere are proportional to r^2

- the *volume* of a sphere is proportional to r^3.

These relationships mean that scaling effects are the same for a sphere as for a cube so, in terms of modelling, a cube is just as good a shape as a sphere. In fact, since cubes can be stacked together into different shapes in a way that spheres cannot, they are more useful in modelling scaling effects.

10.5 Scalars and vectors: distance and displacement

Some quantities have both a *size* and a *direction*. A force is an example – its size can be measured in newtons (N), and it also acts in a particular direction. It is called a **vector** quantity. Other quantities, such as volume, have a size but no direction and are called **scalar** quantities.

This distinction, between vector and scalar quantities, arises when thinking about the movement of things from one place to another. For example, imagine you walk the path as illustrated in Figure 10.8.

Figure 10.8 A simple path

A: 100 metres South

B: 200 metres East

C: 100 metres North

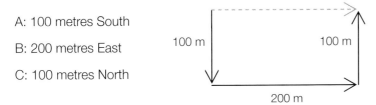

There are two ways of thinking about *how far you have gone*. The first is to think about the length of the path you have walked – in total, 400 metres (100 metres + 200 metres + 100 metres). The second is to think about how far you have ended up from where you started. This is shown by the dotted line: 200 metres East of the start.

The scientific terms for these two ways of expressing how far you have gone are **distance** and **displacement**:

- *Distance*: This is a scalar quantity. It has a size but no direction. For example, the distance for part A of the journey is 100 metres. The total distance for the whole journey (400 metres) can be found by adding the values of the distances for each part of the journey together.

- *Displacement*: This is a vector quantity. It has both a size and a direction. For example, the displacement for part A of the journey is 100 metres South. Finding the displacement for the whole journey (200 metres East) involves more than just adding the sizes together, since the direction needs to be taken into account.

Adding displacements together gets even more complicated if they can be at any angle to each other, not just right angles. This involves using trigonometry (sines, cosines, and so on). This kind of addition of vectors is important in post-16 physics but, for 11–16 science, *calculations* on vector addition are made simple by *only working in one dimension*. However, pupils at this level may be expected to know how to represent the addition of vectors *graphically*, by making scale drawings of situations involving forces.

Figure 10.9 shows an example of vectors in one dimension. It shows displacements for various locations relative to a person's home (shown as 0 m). In this diagram, displacements to the right are indicated by a 'plus' sign, and those to the left by a 'minus' sign (rather than using terms like East and West to indicate direction). This is a very commonly used convention.

Figure 10.9 Displacements in one dimension

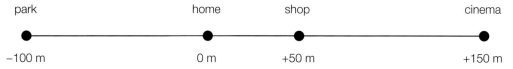

Thus, travelling from home to the shop is a displacement of +50 m, and travelling from the shop to the cinema is a *further* displacement of +100 m. To go from the shop to the park is a total *distance* of 150 m, and as this is in the *left* direction, the *displacement* is −150 m (i.e. negative). Going in the opposite direction, from the park to the shop, is the same distance (150 m), but the displacement is +150 m (i.e. positive). In order to be able to manipulate such vectors, pupils need to know how to add and subtract positive and negative numbers (see Section 9.3 *Operations and symbols* on page 90).

Note that, although working in one dimension makes things simpler, it also means that the vector/scalar distinction is more subtle. The only difference between a distance and a displacement is whether or not there is a sign (+ or −) in front of the value. For movement in two or three dimensions, the differences are more obvious, as the direction is stated in full. However, using the terms distance and displacement correctly is essential. If not, it leads to confusion when it comes to doing calculations and drawing graphs. Unfortunately, this distinction is not always made sufficiently clear.

10.6 Movement of objects: speed and velocity

The **speed** of a moving object is defined as the *distance* it travels in unit time, and the formula is:

$$\text{speed} = \frac{\text{distance}}{\text{time}}$$

Since distance is a **scalar** quantity (i.e. it does not have a direction), speed is also a scalar quantity. The term for *speed in a particular direction* is **velocity** – this is a **vector** quantity and is found from this formula:

$$\text{velocity} = \frac{\text{displacement}}{\text{time}}$$

As its name suggests, the speedometer on a car measures *speed*. A car going at a constant speed along a straight motorway is also moving at a constant velocity, since *its direction stays the same.* However, if it goes round a corner at a constant speed (so that the reading on the speedometer stays the same), its velocity is *not* constant. The velocity is continually changing around a corner since *its direction is changing.*

The formulae for speed and velocity can be rearranged to give the following two equations:

distance $=$ speed $\times$ time

displacement $=$ velocity $\times$ time

The equations both have the form $y = mx$. The first of these equations shows that, if we plot a line graph of *distance* against *time* for a moving object, the **gradient** of the line is its *speed*. Similarly, the second equation shows that if we plot a line graph of *displacement* against *time* for an object moving in one dimension, the gradient of the line is its *velocity*. Such graphs are very useful for showing the behaviour of a moving object, and will be illustrated with an example.

Figure 10.10 shows the journey of a cyclist who travels from home to the cinema, then to the park and back home. (Since the three places are in a straight line it is a one-dimensional journey.) Note that the total distance that the cyclist travels is 500 m (150 m + 250 m + 100 m); however, the total displacement is *zero*, because the cyclist ends up in the same place as at the start.

Figure 10.10 A one-dimensional journey

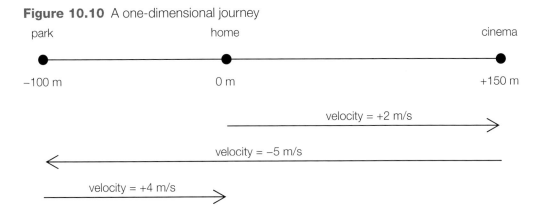

Figure 10.11a shows a **distance–time graph** for this journey. The gradients for each line segment indicate the *speeds* for each part of the journey. The cyclist starts slowly, then speeds up for the second part, and slows down a little at the end. Note that on a distance–time graph, the value for the distance must always get larger over time (you cannot 'undo' the distance travelled), so the gradient of the line is never negative (i.e. it never slopes downwards).

Figure 10.11b shows a **displacement–time graph** for the journey. Although the journey is the same, the appearance of the graph is very different. Here, the gradients for each line segment indicate the *velocities* for each part of the journey. Initially, the velocity is positive (the gradient is positive and slopes upwards), but then the velocity becomes negative (the gradient is negative and slopes downwards). In other words, the cyclist changes direction. After another change in direction, the velocity is positive again and the final value of the displacement is zero (the cyclist is home).

Although the term 'displacement–time graph' is common in school science, strictly speaking, such a graph cannot be drawn since displacement is a *vector*. A graph cannot show both the *size* and *direction* of a quantity. What is called a 'displacement–time graph' actually shows how the *size of the component in a chosen direction of the displacement* of an object changes over time. Such graphs are useful only for objects *moving in a straight line*. A similar point also applies to what are called 'velocity–time graphs' (discussed below), since velocity is also a vector.

In mathematics, the displacement here might be referred to as the 'distance of the cyclist from home', but for a one-dimensional journey these are essentially the same. At the end of the journey, the cyclist's distance from home is zero, and the graph would still have the same shape.

In summary, plotting distance and displacement on a graph can show how these quantities change over time. The rate of change of distance is speed, and the rate of change of displacement is velocity. It is also possible to plot *speed* and *velocity* on a graph to see how these change over time as well.

Figure 10.11 The same journey represented in different ways

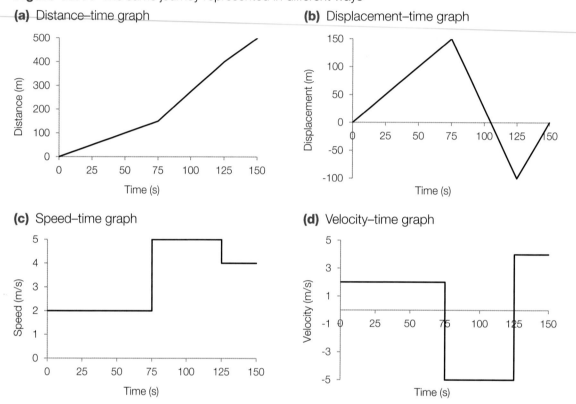

(a) Distance–time graph

(b) Displacement–time graph

(c) Speed–time graph

(d) Velocity–time graph

Figure 10.11c shows a **speed–time graph**, again for the same journey. It shows that, for each of the three stages, the cyclist was travelling at different constant speeds, i.e. each of the lines is horizontal. Figure 10.11d shows a **velocity–time graph**. This also shows three horizontal lines representing constant velocities for each of these stages. The difference here is that the second of these lines is *below* the horizontal axis, indicating that the velocity is *negative*.

10.7 Gradients of lines on speed–time and velocity–time graphs

The gradient of a line on a speed–time graph or a velocity–time graph indicates the rate at which the speed or velocity is changing. This is called *acceleration*. The graphs shown in Figure 10.11 are idealised and do not represent what a real journey would look like, since the changes in speed or velocity happen in zero time. The lines on the graph are vertical: this implies that the acceleration is infinitely large.

A more realistic situation to illustrate the meaning of acceleration is a ball being thrown vertically upwards from the ground and then falling back down to the ground. The change in the ball's height with time is show in Figure 10.12. The changing gradient tells us that, as the ball gets higher, it gets slower and slower until it reaches its maximum height; it then gets faster and faster until it reaches the ground.

Figure 10.12 A ball thrown vertically upwards

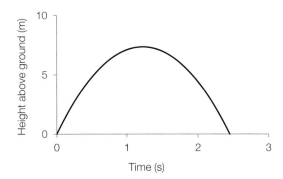

Strictly speaking, *acceleration* is the rate of change of *velocity* (i.e. it is a *vector* quantity), and can be calculated using the formula:

$$\text{acceleration} = \frac{\text{change in velocity}}{\text{time}}$$

However, in school science, it is also commonly used to mean the rate of change of *speed* (i.e. a *scalar* quantity). Because the same word is used to mean two different things, it is important that the context makes it clear whether it is referring to the rate of change of speed or of velocity. A helpful way of making this difference explicit is to talk of a *scalar acceleration* (rate of change of speed) or a *vector acceleration* (rate of change of velocity).

Figure 10.13 shows a speed–time graph and a velocity–time graph for the ball thrown upwards.

Figure 10.13 Representing speed and velocity for a ball thrown vertically upwards

(a) Speed–time graph

(b) Velocity–time graph

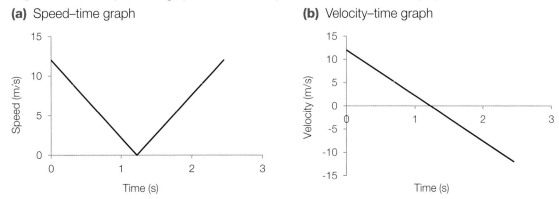

The speed–time graph in Figure 10.13a shows that the ball's speed constantly decreases until it reaches zero (the maximum height) and then steadily increases; in other words, it decelerates and then accelerates. The gradient of the graph represents a *scalar acceleration*: for the first part it is *negative* (the ball is slowing down, or decelerating) and for the second part it is *positive* (the ball is getting faster, or accelerating).

Note that, while it is useful to talk about an object *accelerating* or *decelerating*, the term *deceleration* is better avoided, since only the term *acceleration* represents a quantity with a value.

The velocity–time graph in Figure 10.13b uses the convention that positive values of velocity mean 'going up' and negative values mean 'going down' (values of displacement are taken as positive above ground and negative below it). Here, the gradient has the same *negative* value throughout – it represents a constant *vector acceleration* in the *downwards* direction. The velocity starts with a positive value, decreases until it becomes zero, and continues to decrease when it becomes negative.

Thus, the meaning of a positive or negative acceleration depends on the way the term is being used.

- *Scalar acceleration*: A positive acceleration means getting faster; a negative acceleration means getting slower.

- *Vector acceleration*: The sign (i.e. direction) of the acceleration *on its own* gives no indication whether the ball is getting faster or slower – it depends on the direction of the velocity. An acceleration in the same direction as the velocity (both positive or both negative) means getting faster; an acceleration in a different direction to the velocity (one is positive, the other negative) means getting slower.

10.8 Area under the line on speed–time and velocity–time graphs

On a graph showing a rate of change against time, the **area under the line** is meaningful (see Section 9.13 *Graphs of rates against time: area under the line* on page 105). For a **speed–time graph**, the vertical axis represents the *rate of change of distance* (speed) and the horizontal axis represents *time*. The area under the line then represents *distance*. Figure 10.14a shows the speed–time graph with the areas for each stage of the journey marked. The area of 'A' is $2\,\text{m/s} \times 75\,\text{s}$. This gives $150\,\text{m}$ – the distance travelled in this stage of the journey. Calculating the areas of 'B' and 'C' and then adding all the areas together will give the total distance travelled.

In a similar way, displacement can be found by adding together the areas on a **velocity–time graph**. However, in this case, since velocity can have both positive and negative values, so too can the areas. In Figure 10.14b, the areas of 'A' and 'C' are positive, but 'B' is negative (it is below the horizontal axis). Since for this journey the displacement is zero, the two areas on this graph above the line are equal to the area below, and when they are all added together the total area is zero.

Figure 10.14 Using areas to find distance or displacement

(a) Distance from a speed–time graph **(b)** Displacement from a velocity–time graph

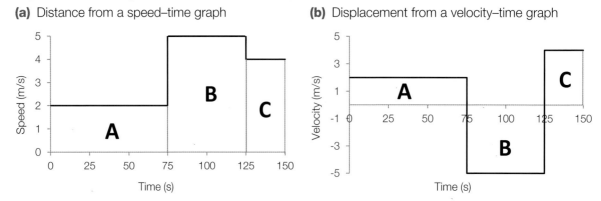

The area under the line on a distance–time graph (distance × time) does not have any real-world meaning, and the same applies to the area under the line on a displacement–time graph (displacement × time). Thus, while the *gradients* of the lines on the four graphs shown in Figure 10.11 all have a real-world meaning, the *areas under the line* are meaningful only for the speed–time and velocity–time graphs.

Glossary for teachers

This glossary contains mathematical terms that are relevant to 11–16 science. The aim is to promote a common understanding of these terms among teachers, publishers, awarding bodies and others. The definitions are not intended for pupils, although it is hoped that they will form a good basis for others to develop glossaries for pupils appropriate to different contexts.

The definitions in the glossary have been kept as consistent as possible with existing sources, where relevant. These include, in particular, *Mathematics Glossary for Teachers in Key Stages 1 to 3* (NCETM) and *The Language of Measurement* (ASE/Nuffield), as well as *Mathematics Glossary for Teachers in Key Stages 1 to 4* (QCA), on which the NCETM glossary was based, and *Signs, Symbols & Systematics: The ASE Companion to 16–19 Science* (ASE). (See *Further references on terminology and conventions* on page 5 in the Introduction for more details of these publications.) The glossary is intended to be complementary to *The Language of Measurement*, and so only those terms from that publication that are essential for the mathematical ideas in the current publication have been included.

Each of the chapters in this publication deals with clusters of key words selected from the list in this glossary. These are included in a panel at the start of each chapter (note that a number of key words appear in more than one chapter). The 'Section' column in the glossary gives links to the sections where the key words are discussed in detail, so the glossary also acts as an index. The key words in the chapters are indicated in **bold italic** text. In the 'Definition' column, *italic terms* are key words than can be found elsewhere in the glossary.

Key words	Definition	Section
algebraic equation	See *equation*.	9.1
anomaly	An anomaly (or anomalous value) is a measured value that appears not to fit the pattern of the other measurements, and is often (though not always) due to a mistake. For example, a value that is very different from the others in a set of repeated measurements, or a *data point* that lies far from a *line of best fit*. See also *outlier*.	6.8
approximation	A value that is not exact, but sufficiently close to the actual value for it to be useful.	2.7
area	A measure of the size of a surface (usually measured in square units, for example cm^2 or m^2).	10.2

Key words	Definition	Section
area under the line (on a graph)	On a graph, the area under a straight line between two values on the *horizontal axis* may have a physical meaning. The area is found by multiplying two values: the *mean* of the values on the *vertical axis*, and the difference between the two values on the horizontal axis. For example, on a *speed–time graph*, the area represents the *mean* (or *average*) *speed* multiplied by the time interval: this gives the *distance* travelled. If a speed–time graph shows a curve rather than a straight line, the area under the curve also represents the distance travelled, though it is not so straightforward to calculate.	9.13, 10.8
arithmetic mean	The sum of a set of values divided by the number of values in the set. Often referred to simply as a *mean* (though there are other types of mean, such as geometric mean).	2.4, 6.5
average	A measure of the 'typical value' of a set of data. Sometimes used synonymously with *mean* (or *arithmetic mean*) even though there are other measures of average, such as *median* and *mode*.	6.5
axis	On a graph or a chart, an axis is a reference line along which distances may represent values of a *variable*. See also *horizontal axis* and *vertical axis*.	4.1
axis label	On the *axis* of a graph, the axis label shows the name of the *variable* and its *unit* where appropriate.	4.1
bar chart	A display for presenting data, in which bars of equal width represent the set of values. Each value is proportional to the length of the bar. The bars may be vertical or horizontal. See also *grouped bar chart* and *stacked bar chart*.	3.3, 3.4, 3.5, 3.7, 4.1, 6.4
base unit	In the International System of Units (SI), there are seven base units. These are the units of the fundamental (and independent) quantities of length (metre), mass (kilogram), time (second), electric current (ampere), temperature (kelvin), chemical amount (mole) and light intensity (candela). See also *derived unit*.	2.1
batch	A set of values related to a single *quantity* or *variable*, for example repeated measurements of the time for a ball to drop a certain distance, or the heights of pupils in a school.	6.4, 8.3, 8.4, 8.5
box plot	A diagram that represents the *distribution* of values in a *batch* of data. The central box represents the *interquartile range*, and the *median* is shown as a line within the box. Lines extend above and below the box to the highest and lowest values.	6.6, 6.7, 8.3, 8.5
brackets	Symbols used to group numbers and letters in *expressions*, and indicating certain operations as having priority. See *order of operations*.	9.4

Key words	Definition	Section
categorical	Categorical data are data that can be sorted into categories (e.g. different 'eye colours' or 'food groups') but cannot be ordered (since they are 'labels' that have no particular order). Categorical data are *qualitative data*.	1.4, 3.2, 6.4
circumference	The distance around a circle (its perimeter).	10.4
class interval	When drawing a *histogram*, the set of *quantitative data* is split into a number of classes (groups). The class interval is the range of values within each class.	6.4
coefficient	In mathematics, a coefficient is a *factor* of an algebraic term, though often it is used to mean a 'numerical coefficient'. For example, in the term $4xy$, 4 is the numerical coefficient of xy, but x is also the coefficient of $4y$ and y is the coefficient of $4x$. In science, the term is also used to apply to the properties of particular materials (e.g. the coefficient of expansion).	9.2
combined events	A combination of two or more events. The *probability* of a combined event can be calculated by multiplying together each of the probabilities of the separate events, but only if these are *independent events*.	6.9
compound measure	In mathematics, a compound measure is one that involves two (or more) other measures of different types. For example, speed (which can be calculated from distance / time) is a compound measure, and has units of metres per second.	2.1
constant	A number or quantity that does not vary. For example, in the *equation* $y = 3x + 6$, the 3 and 6 are constants, where x and y are *variables*. In the general equation for a straight line, $y = mx + c$, m and c are constants for a specific line. In science, the term may be used to refer to 'universal constants' (e.g. the speed of light or the Avogadro constant) or to values that are constant within a particular context (e.g. for a spring that follows Hooke's Law, the value of the spring constant is constant for a specific spring).	5.4, 9.2
constant of proportionality	In a *directly proportional* relationship between two *variables*, x and y, of the form $y = kx$, the *constant k* is referred to as the constant of proportionality.	5.4, 5.5, 5.9, 9.11
continuous	Continuous data are a type of *quantitative data* (numerical data) for which the values can take on any value within a certain range (e.g. the heights of pupils or the temperatures of an object.). See also *discrete*.	1.4, 3.2, 6.4
control variable	In an investigation, the control *variables* are those that are kept constant by the investigator.	1.5
coordinate	On a graph, the coordinates determine the position of each *data point* in relation to the *axes*. See *x-coordinate* and *y-coordinate*.	4.7

Key words	Definition	Section
correlation	A measure of the strength of the association between two *variables*. High correlation implies a close relationship and low correlation a less close one. If an increase in one variable corresponds to an increase in the other, the correlation is positive. If an increase in one variable corresponds to a decrease in the other, the correlation is negative.	8.7
cross-sectional area	The area of a cross-section of a three-dimensional object or geometrical figure. The cross-section is the surface that would be exposed by making a 'straight cut' through the object, often at right angles to an axis of symmetry.	10.3
cube	In geometry, a three-dimensional figure with six identical square faces.	10.2
	In number (arithmetic) and algebra, the result of cubing a number or *expression*. For example, 2^3 (pronounced 'two cubed') is $2 \times 2 \times 2 = 8$.	2.5
cube root	A value whose *cube* is equal to a given value. For example, the cube root of 8 is 2 (since $2^3 = 8$), and this is represented as $\sqrt[3]{8} = 2$ or $8^{1/3} = 2$.	2.5
cuboid	A three-dimensional figure with six rectangular faces. (Some of the rectangular faces may be squares; a *cube* is a special cuboid in which all the faces are squares.)	10.2
data point	On a *line graph* or a *scatter graph*, a data point is represented by a symbol (e.g. $\times$ or $+$). Its position represents a pair of values for the two *variables*.	3.6, 4.1, 4.7
decimal	A term commonly used synonymously with 'decimal fraction', where the number of tenths, hundredths, thousandths, etc. are represented as digits following a decimal point.	2.2
decimal place	In a *decimal*, each column after the decimal point is a decimal place. For example, 5.275 is said to have three decimal places.	2.3
dependent variable	In an investigation, the dependent *variables* are those that are observed or measured by the investigator.	1.5, 3.6, 4.2
derived unit	All SI units, except for the seven *base units*, are derived units. They are produced by suitable multiplication or division involving two or more of the base units.	2.1
diameter	Any straight line segment joining two points on a circle or sphere that passes through the centre.	10.4

Key words	Definition	Section
directly proportional	If the algebraic relation between two *variables*, x and y, is of the form $y = kx$ (where k is a *constant*), y is directly proportional to x. It also follows that x is directly proportional to y (since $x = \frac{1}{k}y$). Another way of expressing this (more common in mathematics than in science) is that x and y are in direct proportion. If y is directly proportional to x, when x is doubled, y also doubles, and when x is multiplied by 10, y is also multiplied by 10. The graphical representation of $y = kx$ is a straight line through the *origin*, where k is the *gradient* of the line. The word 'directly' is often dropped, and the term *proportional* is used to mean the same thing. Using the full term 'directly proportional', however, is helpful when it is being contrasted to *inversely proportional*.	5.2, 9.5, 9.7, 9.11
discrete	Discrete data are a type of *quantitative data* (numerical data) for which the values can take on only certain values. These are often *integer* values produced by counting (e.g. the number of trees in a survey area). See also *continuous*.	1.4, 3.2, 6.4
displacement	The length and direction of the straight line from the initial position of an object to its position at a later time. Displacement is a *vector* quantity.	10.5
displacement–time graph	A graph showing how the *displacement* of an object changes over time.	10.6
distance	The length of the path along which an object has moved. Distance is a *scalar* quantity.	10.5
distance–time graph	A graph showing how the *distance* of an object changes over time.	10.6
distribution	For a set of data, the way in which values in the set are distributed (or spread out) between the highest and lowest values.	6.4, 6.7
equation	A mathematical statement showing that two *expressions* are equal. The expressions are linked with the equals (=) sign. Also referred to as *algebraic equations* where the expressions contain *variables*. A *formula* is an equation that shows the relationship between real-world variables. In science, the term 'equation' is also used to refer to a chemical equation.	9.1, 9.2, 9.3, 9.11
estimate	A rough or approximate value, found by calculating with suitable *approximations* or using previous experience.	2.7
experiment	An investigation in which variables may be manipulated and data are collected by observing the effects of changing some of the variables. See also *survey*.	1.5

Key words	Definition	Section
exponent	In *index notation*, the term 'exponent' is used synonymously with *index*.	2.5
exponential relationship	A relationship between two *variables*, x and y, of the form $y = a^x$. For example, if $a = 2$, each increase of 1 for x corresponds to a doubling of y.	9.11
expression	A mathematical form expressed symbolically, consisting of a combination of numbers and *variables* that may be evaluated. Expressions do not contain the equals ($=$) sign.	9.1, 9.3, 9.4
extrapolation	On a graph, extrapolation means estimating the value of one *variable* from a value of the other, using a *line of best fit* that is extended beyond the *range* of the available data. Care needs to be taken, since the relationship may not apply outside the data range. See also *interpolation*.	7.5
factor	In an investigation, an independent *variable* is often referred to as a factor, particularly when it is a *categorical* variable. In mathematics, the term has an entirely different meaning: when a number can be expressed as the product of two or more numbers, these are factors of the first. For example, 2 and 3 are factors of 6.	1.5, 3.2, 3.4, 3.5
formula	An *equation* that shows the relationship between real-world *variables*. By rearranging the formula, it is possible to make any of the other variables the *subject of the formula*. In science, the term 'formula' is also used to refer to a chemical formula.	9.1, 9.4, 9.5, 9.6, 9.7, 9.8, 9.9
fraction	The result of dividing one *integer* by a second integer, which must be non-zero.	2.2
frequency	In statistics, the number of times an event occurs, or the number of individuals or objects with some specific property. (Although it is a very different context, in science, the frequency of a wave or an oscillation has a related meaning – the number of cycles per unit of time.)	3.2, 6.4
frequency table	A table showing the *frequencies* of objects or events in different categories or *class intervals*.	3.2
gradient	On a graph, the gradient is a measure of the steepness of a line, and is calculated by dividing the vertical change by the corresponding horizontal change. It represents the *rate* at which the *variable* plotted on the *vertical axis* changes with the variable plotted on the *horizontal axis*.	3.6, 5.3, 7.2, 7.3, 9.12, 10.6, 10.7
grouped bar chart	A type of *bar chart* used to represent data categorised by two *factors*. Each group of bars represents one factor, and the bars within each group represent the other factor. (Also known as a clustered bar chart.)	3.5

Key words	Definition	Section
grouped data	*Discrete* data and *continuous* data can be grouped into *class intervals* and counted to produce a *frequency table*. This is called grouped data.	3.2
histogram	In science, the term 'histogram' is used to refer to a representation of the *distribution* of data, in which the height of each bar is *proportional* to the *frequency* of values in each class: all of the *class intervals* are equal, and the bars are of equal width. In mathematics and statistics, the class intervals may not all be equal, and so the bars may be of different widths. The area of each bar is proportional to the frequency of values in each class, and the height of each rectangle represents the 'frequency density' of the class.	6.4, 6.7, 8.3
horizontal axis	On a *line graph* or a *scatter graph*, the horizontal axis usually represents the *independent variable*. (See also *x-axis*.)	3.6, 4.1, 4.2, 5.3
independent events	Two events are independent if the *probability* of the second event is not affected by the outcome of the first.	6.9
independent variable	In an investigation, the independent *variables* are those that are changed by the investigator.	1.5, 3.6, 4.2
index	In *index notation*, the superscript is called the index, for example in a^4 the index is 4. (Note that the plural of index is indices.) It is also possible to have fractional and negative indices.	2.5
index notation	The notation in which a product such as $a \times a \times a \times a$ is recorded as a^4.	2.5
integer	Any of the positive or negative whole numbers and zero (e.g. ..., −2, −1, 0, +1, +2, ...).	1.4, 2.3
intercept	On a graph, the point at which a straight line or a curve crosses an *axis* is called an intercept. The term 'intercept' is typically used in relation to the *vertical axis* (*y-axis*), but also applies to the *horizontal axis* (*x-axis*).	7.2, 7.6, 9.11, 9.12
interpolation	On a graph, interpolation means estimating the value of one *variable* from a value of the other, using a *line of best fit* that does not extend beyond the *range* of the data. See also *extrapolation*.	7.5
interquartile range	The difference between the upper and lower *quartiles*. It contains the middle half of the values in the ordered data set. It is a useful measure of *spread* since, unlike the *range*, it is not much affected by *outliers*.	6.6, 8.3

Key words	Definition	Section
inverse	Inverse operations are 'opposite' operations that 'undo each other'. For example, subtraction is the inverse of addition, and -5 is the additive inverse of 5 since their sum is zero. Division is the inverse of multiplication, and ⅓ is the multiplicative inverse of 3 since their product is 1. (Sometimes, the term is used synonymously with *reciprocal*, for example 'the inverse of 2 is ½'.)	5.4
inverse square relationship	A relationship between two *variables*, x and y, of the form $y = a/x^2$, where a is a *constant*.	9.11
inversely proportional	If the algebraic relation between two *variables*, x and y, is of the form $y = k/x$ (where k is a *constant*), y is inversely proportional to x. It also follows that x is inversely proportional to y (since $x = k/y$). Another way of expressing the equation is $xy = k$. If y is inversely proportional to x then, for example, when x is doubled, y is halved, and when x is multiplied by 10, y is divided by 10.	5.4, 5.5, 9.5, 9.7, 9.11
line graph	In mathematics, a line graph is a graph in which adjacent *data points* are joined by straight-line segments. Such graphs are also used in science. However, a 'line graph' in science more often refers to a graph where it is assumed that there is a simple relationship between the two *variables*, such that a *line of best fit* can be drawn that is very close to all the *data points*. In practice, not all the data points fit on this line because of measurement *uncertainty*.	3.3, 3.6, 4.1, 5.2, 7.1, 7.2, 9.11, 9.12, 9.13
line of best fit	A line drawn on a graph that passes through or as close as possible to the *data points*. It represents the best estimate of any underlying relationship between the *variables*. A 'line of best fit' often refers to a straight line but it may also be a curve.	7.4, 8.8
linear	On a graph, a relationship is said to be linear if it is represented by a straight line. See also *linear relationship*.	7.2
linear dimension	A term often used in the context of scaling. A linear dimension refers to the distance between two points of a geometric figure. When comparing two similar geometric figures, the *scale factor* applies only to the linear dimensions (any two corresponding lengths), and not to the area or volume.	5.9, 10.3, 10.4
linear relationship	If the relationship between two *variables*, x and y, is *linear*, equal changes in x correspond to equal changes in y. For example, with a spring that follows Hooke's Law, for each additional 100 g mass suspended from the spring, its length increases by the same amount as before. The equation for a linear relationship can be expressed in the form $y = mx + c$. When represented as a graph, this is a straight line for which m is the *gradient* of the line and c is the *intercept* on the *y-axis*.	7.2, 7.4, 9.11

Key words	Definition	Section
mass	A measure of the quantity of matter in an object. The SI *base unit* of mass is the kilogram (kg). In science, it is important to distinguish between mass and *weight*.	10.1
mean	The sum of a set of values divided by the number of values in the set. (More correctly called the *arithmetic mean*, as there are also other types of mean, such as geometric mean.) See also *average*.	2.4, 6.5
median	The middle value in a set of data when all the values are arranged in order. An equal number of data values lie above and below the median. See also *average*.	6.5, 8.3
mode	The most commonly occurring value in a set of *discrete* data. Some sets of data may have more than one mode. See also *average*.	6.5
non-linear	A non-linear relationship is one that is not *linear* and, on a graph, is represented by a curve and not by a straight line. See also *linear relationship*.	7.2
order of magnitude	The approximate size, often given as a *power of 10*. Orders of magnitude are particularly useful when comparing values of very different sizes. For example, 4763 is very roughly 1000 times larger than 3.8, i.e. 10^3 or 'three orders of magnitude larger'.	2.6, 2.7
order of operations	The order in which different mathematical operations are applied in a calculation. The convention is often encapsulated in the mnemonic BIDMAS (Brackets, Indices, Division/Multiplication, Addition/Subtraction) or BODMAS (where O represents Order or 'to the power Of').	9.4
origin	On a graph, the origin is the point at which the values of both *variables* are zero (the *x-coordinate* and the *y-coordinate* are both zero).	4.3, 5.2, 7.2, 7.6, 9.11
outlier	A value in a set of data that is judged to be unusually large or unusually small in comparison with most of the other values, for whatever reason. In sampling a population, an outlier may indicate an individual with exceptional characteristics. By contrast, an outlier in a set of repeated measurements may indicate that a mistake has been made (see also *anomaly*).	6.8, 7.7, 8.3
percentage	A fraction expressed as the number of parts per hundred and recorded using the notation %.	5.8
percentile	When the values in a *batch* of data are arranged in order, the percentiles are the values that split the data into 100 groups containing (as far as possible) equal numbers of values. For example, 10% of the data values lie below the 10th percentile. See also *quartile*.	8.3

Key words	Definition	Section
pie chart	A display for presenting data, in which the sectors (like 'slices of a pie') represent the proportions of each of the values. The size of each value is *proportional* to the angle at the centre of the circle.	3.3, 3.4, 3.5
population	In statistics, a population is the entire collection of objects or events of a similar nature that are of interest in a study, and about which data may be collected. This is usually done by selecting a *sample*.	6.3, 8.2
power	In *index notation*, the term 'power' is often used synonymously with *index*. Using the term 'power' in its correct sense, the expression 3^4 can be described as 'the fourth power of 3'.	2.5
power of 10	Any number of the form 10^n is called a *power* of 10, where n is an *integer* (negative, zero, or positive), for example ... 10^{-2}, 10^{-1}, 10^0, 10^1, 10^2, 10^3 (i.e. 0.01, 0.1, 1, 10, 100, 1000). Each number in the series is 10 times the previous number.	2.6
primary data	Data collected directly by the user. See also *raw data* and *secondary data*.	1.5
probability	The likelihood of an event happening. Probability is expressed on a scale from 0 to 1. Where an event cannot happen its probability is 0 and where it is certain its probability is 1.	6.9
proportional	The term 'proportional' is often used to mean the same as *directly proportional*. Using the full term 'directly proportional', however, is helpful when it is being contrasted to *inversely proportional*.	5.1, 5.2, 5.4, 5.5, 5.7, 7.2, 7.6, 9.9, 9.11
qualitative data	Data that are non-numerical (in contrast to *quantitative data*). See also *categorical*.	1.1, 6.4
quantitative data	Data that are numerical (in contrast to *qualitative data*). See also *continuous* and *discrete*.	1.1, 6.4
quantity	Any property that can be given a magnitude by measuring or counting.	1.1, 2.1
quartile	When the values in a *batch* of data are arranged in order, the quartiles are the three values that split the data into four groups containing (as far as possible) equal numbers of values. They are called the first or lower quartile, the second quartile (or *median*), and the third or upper quartile. The difference between the upper and lower quartiles is the *interquartile range*.	6.6, 8.3
radius	The distance from the centre of a circle or sphere to any point on the circle or sphere.	10.4
random error	A component of measurement error due to measurements varying in unpredictable ways from one measurement to the next.	6.2

Key words	Definition	Section
random sample	A *sample* from a *population* in which all the individuals in the population are selected at random and have an equal chance of being included in the sample.	8.2
range	For a measuring instrument, the range is the set of values that can be measured, describing its lower and upper limits.	1.2
	In an *experiment* investigating the relationship between two *quantitative variables*, the range refers to the lowest and highest values of a variable. For the *independent variable* the range is chosen by the experimenter and for the *dependent variable* the range is determined by the results of the experiment.	4.3, 4.5
	On a graph, the range of an *axis* indicates the highest and lowest values on the axis.	4.3, 4.4
	For a *distribution* of data, the range is a measure of *spread*, and is the difference between the highest and lowest values. Note that in school science, the term 'range' is generally used to indicate both the lowest and highest values themselves, and not the difference between them.	6.6, 8.3
rate	A measure of how quickly one *variable* changes in comparison with another variable. For example, *speed* is the rate of change of *distance* with time.	5.3, 7.3, 9.12, 9.13
ratio	A ratio shows the relative sizes of two values, usually written in the form $a : b$ (and pronounced 'the ratio of a to b'). Since a ratio is a comparison of two similar quantities, it does not have *units*.	5.6
raw data	Data collected directly from *experiments* or *surveys*, before being processed. See also *primary data*.	1.5, 3.2
reciprocal	The reciprocal of a value is 1 divided by the value; for example, the reciprocal of 2 is ½.	2.5, 5.4
recurring decimal	A decimal with an infinitely repeating digit or group of digits (e.g. the fraction ⅓ is the decimal 0.33333…).	2.3
resolution	The resolution of a measuring instrument is the smallest change in the quantity being measured that gives a perceptible change in the indication on the instrument.	1.2
risk	Risk is related to the *probability* of harm occurring when exposed to a hazard. The actual value of a risk is often called the 'absolute risk', while a 'relative risk' may be used to compare the risks for two different situations or groups (e.g. in a clinical trial, to compare the risks for the control group and for the treatment group).	6.10, 6.11
round	'Rounding a number' means expressing it as an *approximation* with fewer *significant figures*. For example, 5.432 rounded to the nearest 0.1 is 5.4 (from four to two significant figures).	2.3

Key words	Definition	Section
sample	A subset of a *population*. In collecting data, a sample of observations may be made from which to draw inferences about a larger population.	6.3, 8.2
scalar	A *quantity* that has a magnitude (size) but no direction, for example *mass*. See also *vector*.	10.5, 10.6
scale	Used as a noun: a set of marks on a line with equal intervals. Applies to: • an analogue measuring instrument • the *axis* on a graph. Used as a verb: to enlarge or reduce a number, quantity or measurement by a given amount (called a *scale factor*).	 1.2 4.4, 4.5 5.9
scale drawing	A representation of a physical object in which all lengths in the drawing are in the same *ratio* (the *scale factor*) to the corresponding lengths in the actual object.	5.9, 10.3
scale factor	In a *scale drawing*, the *ratio* of any length in the drawing to the corresponding length in the physical object. More generally, the scale factor for two similar geometric figures is the ratio of any two corresponding lengths.	5.9, 10.3
scatter graph	A graph on which paired values for two *variables* are plotted and which may indicate a relationship between the variables. On a scatter graph, it is not meaningful to join the *data points* with line segments, but a *line of best fit* may be drawn.	3.3, 3.6, 4.1, 8.7, 8.8
scientific notation	See *standard form*.	2.6
secondary data	Data obtained indirectly from sources such as books, articles or web pages. See also *primary data*.	1.5
significant figures	The number of digits that contribute information about the size of a value (related to the measurement *uncertainty*).	1.2, 2.3
slope	Sometimes used as an informal alternative to *gradient*, although gradient is the preferred term.	5.3
speed	The rate of change of *distance* with time. Speed is a *scalar* quantity.	10.6
speed–time graph	A graph showing how the *speed* of an object changes over time.	10.6, 10.7, 10.8
spread	For a *batch* of values, the term 'spread' refers to how close together or far apart the values are. Measures of spread include the *range*, *interquartile range* and standard deviation.	6.6
square	In geometry, a two-dimensional figure with four equal sides and four right angles. In number (arithmetic) and algebra, the result of squaring a number or *expression*. For example, 5^2 (pronounced 'five squared') is $5 \times 5 = 25$.	10.2 2.5

Key words	Definition	Section
square root	A value whose *square* is equal to a given value. For example, a square root of 25 is 5 (since $5^2 = 25$), and this is recorded as $\sqrt{25} = 5$. It also has a negative square root (-5), since $(-5)^2 = 25$.	2.5
stacked bar chart	A type of *bar chart* used to represent data categorised by two *factors*. Each bar represents one factor, and the segments within each bar represent the other factor. (Also known as a compound bar chart.)	3.5
standard form	A form in which numbers are recorded as a number between 1 and 10 multiplied by a *power of 10*. For example, 193 in standard form is recorded as 1.93×10^2. It is also referred to as *standard index form* and *scientific notation*.	2.6
standard index form	See *standard form*.	2.6
stem-and-leaf diagram	A format for organising the values in a *batch* of data. The *class intervals* are represented on the vertical 'stem', and the values in each class interval are represented as horizontal rows forming the 'leaves'.	8.3
subject of a formula	A *formula* is an *equation* that shows the relationship between real-world *variables*. It is conventionally written so that one of these variables is 'on its own' on the left of the equals sign – this variable is called the subject of the formula. By rearranging the formula, it is possible to make any of the other variables the subject of the formula.	9.6, 9.7, 9.8
surface area	The area of the surface of a three-dimensional object or geometric figure.	10.3
surface area : volume ratio	The ratio of the *surface area* to the *volume* for a three-dimensional object or geometric figure.	10.3
survey	An investigation in which variables are hard to manipulate, and data are collected from *samples* of *populations*. See also *experiment*.	1.5
tangent	On a graph, a straight line that touches a curve at only one point. The line has the same *gradient* as the gradient of the curve at that point. (The term is also used in trigonometry: the tangent of an angle in a right-angled triangle is the ratio of the length of the opposite side to the length of the adjacent side.)	9.12
tick mark	On a graph or chart, the tick marks are the small lines along the *axis* at regular intervals, each representing a value on the *scale*.	4.1
tick mark label	On a graph or chart, the number next to a *tick mark* indicating the size of the value.	4.1
time series	A set of observations, generally measurements or counts, taken over time and usually at equally spaced intervals.	1.5, 3.6, 4.2
true value	The value that would be obtained in an ideal measurement.	6.2

Key words	Definition	Section
two-way table	A *frequency table* in which the *frequencies* are categorised by two independent *factors* (*categorical* variables).	3.2
uncertainty	The interval within which the true value can be expected to lie, with a given level of confidence or *probability*.	6.2
unit	A unit of measurement is a standard used in measuring (e.g. the metre is a unit of length; the kilogram is a unit of mass).	1.1, 2.1, 3.1, 4.6
unit prefix	The prefix used to form a decimal multiple or submultiple of an SI *unit* (e.g. 'kilo' or 'milli').	2.6
value	The value of a *quantity* or a *variable* may be a number, or may consist of a number and a *unit*.	1.1
variability	Variability in a set of data relates to how spread out or how close together the values are. It may arise due to measurement *uncertainty* or due to differences between the individuals in a *population*.	6.1, 6.2, 6.3, 8.3
variable	In an investigation: a physical, chemical or biological quantity or characteristic that can differ from case to case.	1.3, 1.5, 2.1, 3.1, 7.2, 8.7
	In an algebraic equation: a quantity that can take on a range of values, often denoted by a letter (e.g. x, y, z, t).	1.5, 2.1, 9.2
vector	A *quantity* that has both a magnitude (size) and a direction, for example *displacement*. See also *scalar*.	10.5, 10.6
velocity	The rate of change of *displacement* with time. Velocity is a *vector* quantity.	10.6
velocity–time graph	A graph showing how the *velocity* of an object changes over time.	10.6, 10.7, 10.8
vertical axis	On a *line graph* or a *scatter graph*, the vertical axis usually represents the *dependent variable*. (See also *y-axis*.)	3.6, 4.1, 4.2, 5.3
volume	A measure of three-dimensional space (usually measured in cubic units, for example cm^3, dm^3 or m^3).	10.2
weight	The weight of an object can be defined as the gravitational force exerted on the object. Its SI *derived unit* is the newton (N). In everyday language, it is common for 'weight' to be measured in units of *mass*, for example grams (g) or kilograms (kg). In science, however, it is important to distinguish between weight and mass.	10.1
x-axis	On a graph, the x-axis is the *horizontal axis*.	4.1, 4.2, 5.3
x-coordinate	On a graph, the x-coordinate of a *data point* is its distance along the *x-axis*.	4.1, 4.7, 5.3
y-axis	On a graph, the y-axis is the *vertical axis*.	4.1, 4.2, 5.3
y-coordinate	On a graph, the y-coordinate of a *data point* is its distance along the *y-axis*.	4.1, 4.7, 5.3